淘淨
銅砂

The CHEMICAL ARTS
of OLD CHINA

李喬苹著

中國古代之化學工藝

胡適題

The CHEMICAL ARTS
of OLD CHINA

by
Li Ch'iao-p'ing
Professor of Chemistry
National Northeastern University
Mukden, China

with a foreword by
Tenney L. Davis

Published by
JOURNAL OF CHEMICAL EDUCATION
Easton, Pennsylvania

FOREWORD

Professor Li's book on "The Chemical Arts of Old China" will interest students of chemistry and of the history of chemistry, also sinologists, and students of the culture, of the economics, and of the arts and crafts of Asia. It will be well-nigh indispensable to importers of Chinese goods and to curators of museum collections of Chinese art objects and antiquities. It covers a field which is not covered, so far as I know, by any other book in English. Its principal defect is in not being long enough.

When Professor Li wrote me that he had prepared an English language version of his book (which had already been published in Chinese and in Japanese), and expressed a desire to find an American publisher for it, I asked to see it, I read it, I liked it, and I brought it to the attention of the *Journal of Chemical Education*. The Journal's reaction was like my own, and now we have the Journal to thank for making it possible for us—for those of us who enjoy these studies—to procure the book and to have it on our shelves. We have benefited greatly from the advice and assistance of Professor James R. Ware while seeing the book through the press.

While reading the book, I have repeatedly found myself wishing that the author had gone into greater detail, that he had given us more on every one of the subjects which he discusses. This, however, would have made the book much larger. On some of his subjects, too, particularly on Chinese alchemy, on gunpowder, and on paper manufacture, there is already printed in English, though scattered in various publications, considerable material of which he has taken no account. The addition of this material would destroy the balance and symmetry of his work, well rounded as it is. We have resisted the temptation to add footnotes and references to studies by Occidental scholars. The book, as fully as we could leave it, is the work of Professor Li.

Professor Li Ch'iao-p'ing has taught at National Peiping University, then at China University in Peiping, and is at present professor of Chemistry at National Northeastern University in Mukden where he gives courses in industrial chemistry, in chemical analysis, and in the chemistry of fermentation. He also teaches chemistry at National Shen Yang Medical College in Mukden. In addition to the present book, he has written two textbooks in the Chinese language, "Industrial Organic Chemistry," 1933, and "Inorganic Chemistry," 1936, both published by the Commercial Press, Ltd., Shanghai, China.

TENNEY L. DAVIS

PREFACE

Foreigners, when they discuss Chinese culture, have a tendency to admire only the high achievements of philosophy and literature and to pay but very little attention to China's work in the practical arts. At the end of the Ch'ing Dynasty or late in the nineteenth century, when the Chinese first made close contact with European civilization and with its applied science, when they saw the highly developed state of science in European countries, instead of treating this science with due respect, some of our countrymen declared that all the important scientific discoveries of European countries had already been made by the Chinese long ago. In order to support this view they produced many specious proofs and doubtful examples. Such an idea still prevails in certain Chinese circles, and statements to this effect are sometimes quoted by foreign authors. This holds true for the study of chemistry in China.

With regard to the history of chemistry in China, it is of course unnecessary to make exaggerated claims. On the other hand, we should not overlook the real contributions made by our ancestors to this subject. The study of modern chemistry in China began in the last century, but certain achievements which were made long ago should not be ignored. To write such a history it is necessary to examine carefully all important Chinese literature bearing on the subject, in addition, to inquire into existing native industrial methods. Furthermore, the old statements of the early writers ought to be interpreted in a most careful manner from the viewpoint of modern scientific chemistry.

No detailed and systematic statement on the history of chemistry in China having been published heretofore, a work on this subject may be of importance to both historians and chemists. The writer, who has spent his last twenty years in the study of industrial chemistry and, at the same time, has a deep interest in Chinese history, ventures to hope that this book may perhaps be of some value as a basis for further investigations.

The book was first written in Chinese, entitled "History of Chemistry in China," and published by the Commercial Press, Ltd., Shanghai, China. The first edition appeared in 1940, and the second edition in 1941. It was also translated into Japanese under the title, "History of Industrial Chemistry in China," and published in 1941. With additional material this English version, "The Chemical Arts of Old China," was completed in the same year but its publication was postponed because of the war. The author wishes to express his sincere gratitude to those of his friends who have assisted in preparing this edition, especially to Dr. Tenney L. Davis for proofreading the manuscript, for writing the Foreword, and for seeing the book through the press; to Professor James R. Ware for attending to many matters which will make the book more acceptable to sinologists; and finally to Dr. Hu Shih for writing the Chinese title page.

LI CH'IAO-P'ING

10A Hua Yuan Ta Yuan,
Fu Ch'ien Chieh, Peiping, China

CONTENTS

THE CHEMICAL ARTS
of OLD CHINA

Chapter 1—INTRODUCTION

THE word for chemistry is "*hua hsüeh*" (化學) in Chinese, which means literally "the study of change." This phrase, however, does not occur in old Chinese literature. It is, indeed, a new term, adopted when modern scientific chemistry was introduced into China from Europe in the latter part of the Ch'ing Dynasty. Although we are not quite sure of the exact date of the earliest occurrence of this term in Chinese, or when it first appeared in Chinese, it is said that the oldest books on chemistry written in the Chinese language are probably the *Hua hsüeh chien Yüan* (化學鑑源), or "Principles of Chemistry," and the *Hua hsüeh ch'u chieh* (化學初階), or the "First Course in Chemistry." The first book was written by Hsü Shou (徐壽), but its year of publication is not known. The second book was written by Ho Liao-jan (何瞭然) and was published in the 9th year of T'ung-chih (同治) of the Ch'ing Dynasty, that is, in the year 1870. Chemistry, as well as other sciences in China, attracted the attention of the Chinese after the Sino-Japanese War of 1894, and especially after the Boxer Protocol in 1901. Since 1901 chemistry has been taught as a regular course in the Chinese universities, colleges, and middle schools, and laboratory experiments, at first of a simple kind, have been included as part of the instruction.

We must admit that before the nineteenth century there was no such science as chemistry in China. The Chinese, of course, were well acquainted with the different kinds of

metals, such as gold, silver, iron, copper, etc., but they did
not realize that they are fundamental chemical elements.
Although the word *"ch'i"* (氣)—air or spirit—occurred early
in Chinese literature, the Chinese did not know that air is
composed of oxygen and nitrogen. In the same way, while
in their daily life they made frequent contact with fire and
water, they did not understand the actual chemical phenomena of fire or the chemical composition of water.

However, if we were to study Chinese literature and history, we should be inclined to say that, although chemistry
in the sense of the modern science did not exist in China before the nineteenth century, investigations and achievements
in chemistry, nevertheless, had been made very early in
Chinese history. Properly enough, legend claims that the
Chinese began to make salt as early as the time of the Yellow
Emperor (one of the Five), and to make wine as early as the
Hsia Dynasty. Paper and porcelain, on the other hand, seem
to start with the Han Dynasty (206 B.C.–A.D. 220). Alchemical practices are assigned to the time of the Yellow
Emperor and were popular under the Chou (1122–255 B.C.)
and subsequent dynasties. We know that alchemy was the
forerunner of chemistry and that the processes of manufacturing salt, paper, wine, and porcelain are important applications of industrial chemistry in the modern world. There is,
therefore, no doubt that in China the practice and study of
applied chemistry has had a long history. Although it has
been stated that the application of such chemical arts as
metallurgy, baking of pottery, etc., were first achieved in
ancient Egypt, yet remains of a similar activity, dating from
the last half of the second millenium B.C. are also found in
northern China.

The Chinese had a theory to interpret natural phenomena, and reduce their apparent complexity to simple, unifying
terms. This theory, like the old Chinese theory of medicine,
is actually philosophical rather than scientific. All the im-

portant chemical phenomena are interpreted through the so-called "*yin*," or the negative element, and "*yang*," or the positive element, and sometimes also through the so-called "*wu-hsing*" (五行) or five "elements"—metal, wood, water, fire, and earth. Everything in the universe is produced, according to this theory, by the mutual interaction of the above-mentioned elements, because water can be mixed with earth, earth can be hardened by the action of fire, fire can melt metal, metal can be used to cut wood, wood can be burnt into ashes and in turn changed into earth. To be specific, the explosive property of gunpowder was regarded as the interaction of "*yin*" and "*yang*" and it was considered that the niter of gunpowder has the property of "*yin*," or negative, element, and the sulfur has the property of "*yang*," or positive element, and that the sudden violent impact of the positive and negative elements produces a very strong force which can blow up everything in its way (see *T'ien kung k'ai wu* [1637], ch. 15.31 (天工開物). Fermentation in the process of making wine was also interpreted by the same theory. Chinese wine is made from rice and ferment. Rice was considered as the "*yang*" or positive element, whereas the ferment was the "*yin*" or negative element. The meeting of these two elements produces an intense heat, which is the actual cause of the fermentation and the wine is accordingly produced in this way (*Chiu shih* (酒史), Ming ed., 6.2a). The theory of Chinese Alchemy, as will be explained in detail in the next chapter, is also entirely based on similar ideas.

However, although the Chinese have tried to explain all kinds of chemical phenomena by means of the theory of "*yin*" and "*yang*" or by that of "*wu hsing*," they have also ascribed to the mysterious power of devils or gods those phenomena that could not be accounted for by the above-mentioned theories. For instance, the occasional failure to get proper fermentation in the processes of wine-making has not been attributed to a temperature unsuitable to the growth of the ferment, but rather to some punishment inflicted by the wine god. There were many such examples among the Chinese, and even today in every Chinese industrial chemical plant a god of the respective industry is installed, and seasonal sacrifice is piously offered.

While these theories are entirely philosophical, a careful study of them, such as is undertaken in the following chapters, shows their importance for a knowledge of the historical development of chemistry in the world. It is interesting to note that certain Chinese theories of chemistry have occasionally resembled those of modern times. It is stated in the *Pen ts'ao kang mu* ch. 8.1 (本草綱目), the Chinese Materia Medica, that the different kinds of metals and precious stones were formed by the condensation of different kinds of heavy aërial elements, and that the different colors are the result of the interaction of different kinds of light aërial elements. The Chinese also believed in the existence of the two fundamental elements *"yin"* and *"yang"* in the air and they thought that it was these two elements reacting with other objects which produced the various kinds of things that differ from one another in having more *"yin"* or more *"yang"* (See Fang I Chih: *Wu li hsiao shih* (方以知物理小識) A Short Description of Physics.)

Through such a philosophical theory of chemistry, the ancient Chinese, nevertheless, succeeded in making certain valuable contributions to industrial chemistry. Certain products of this industry, such as porcelain, colors, lacquer, wine, and soybean sauce, enjoy even today a good name in the world. The modern method of using lactic acid in the process of alcohol-making, according to the interpretation given later, coincides with the principle of using the sour rice-scouring water in the making of Chinese wine, which was a method applied very early by the ancient Chinese people. The recently invented amylo process of alcoholic fermentation is said to have been made by the using of certain special species of mold which occur in Chinese leaven. The manufacture of pigments in ancient China has also been admired by Europeans.

It may be concluded that the successful applications of chemistry accomplished by the Chinese in early times were mostly due to their keen observation and to the clever utilization of their daily experience. It seems to us that their real contributions gained little from their particular theories, for the latter were created, in the main, after the discoveries had been made and were used only with the object of interpreting the established facts.

The present book is written for the purpose of describing in detail the theory, the method, and the history of the various important branches of ancient Chinese chemistry, particularly alchemy, metallurgy and smelting, salt-making, ceramics, pyrotechnics, tanning, and the manufacture of lacquers, colors, oils and fats, wine, bean-sauce, sugar, paper, and incense. If the facts are fully and properly considered, it will be easier to compare Chinese civilization with that of other countries as far as chemistry is concerned. The Chinese, for their part, will understand better how to utilize the valuable contributions to chemistry made by their ancestors, and try to achieve greater things in this field than have been achieved by former investigators.

Chapter 2—ALCHEMY

A STUDY of the ancient history of chemistry in Europe shows that in the earliest days alchemy played a great role. In ancient China, too, many people interested themselves in such mysteries. The principal endeavor of the Chinese alchemists was to discover how to prepare the so-called *chin tan* (金丹), a medicine which it was thought would prolong life. The transmutation of metals seems to have been a secondary object. With these two fanciful ideas they enthralled many people, especially emperors and kings, for a very long time.

It is rather difficult to ascertain when the study of alchemy in China began. The oral traditions of Taoism attribute it, of course, to the Yellow Emperor and also to Lao tzu (?604–500? B.C.), but the Chou period—about 400–255 B.C.—would seem to be historically sounder.

During that time, a native of Yen—now Hopei—named Sung Wu-chi (宋無忌) was called "Fire Immortal" (火仙) because he was thought to be a "Spirit of Fire." Another man named Hsien-men Tzu-kao (羨門子高) was also said to be an immortal. Both of them professed to have the power of bestowing immortality and to hold the secret of the transmutation of metals. King Wei-hsüan (威宣), of Ch'i, and King Chao (昭), of Yen, were very much bewitched by them and consequently sent people abroad to find P'eng-lai (蓬萊), Fang-chang (方丈), and Jen-chou (瀛洲)—the three isles of immortality—where, so it was believed, drugs to make men immortal could be found.

6

Figure 1. Ko Hung (about A.D. 281–361), the greatest of the Chinese alchemists.

Later, there was a Taoist by the name of Hsü Fu (徐福) who memorialized the First Emperor of Ch'in (246–210 B.C.), seeking permission to fast, to abstain from the killing of animals, and to go with a party of unsullied lads and maidens to search for these drugs. The Emperor agreed to send him but nothing was obtained. It was never known where they went for they never returned.

Therefore Ssu-ma Ch'ien (163–85 B.C.), the famous Chinese historian, author of *Shih chi*—Historical Records—collected the facts as stated above and made the following statement in his account of *Feng* and *Shan* (封禪書), ch. 28.11:

Kings Wei-hsüan and Chao sent men abroad to find P'eng-lai, Fang-chang, and Jen-chou. These three islands were said to be in the midst of the Po Hai (渤海). They are not far distant from the mainland but, unfortunately, just as one is at the point of arriving at the islands, one's boat is driven back by the wind and one finds oneself far away from them. In ancient times—to tell the truth—there were people who succeeded in reaching the isles. On them immortals live, and the drug which prevents death can be found there. There all things, even birds and quadrupeds, are made of gold and silver. No one has succeedeed in reaching the isles a second time. People have seen them from a distance like a cloud, but when they approached, the isles became submerged in the sea and when they got quite near the wind suddenly forced their boat out to open sea. In short, no one has been able to land, but Emperors and Kings remained credulous and hopeful of eventual success.

When the First Emperor of the Ch'in Dynasty controlled the whole of China, he found when he reached the seashore many alchemists there, talking about the islands and the drugs of immortality. The Emperor was afraid that he would be too late even if he reached the isles at all, so he sent off men to lead the lads and maidens to the isles, but it was generally said that when the boat got out to sea it was blown back by the wind. It was impossible to reach the islands. They could only be looked at from a distance.

As the Emperor wanted to hold his throne perpetually, he sent Lu Sheng (蘆生), a native of Yen, to ask Hsien-men Tzu-kao, an alchemist, about the fortune of Ch'in. After Lu Sheng came back he memorialized the Emperor, stating that Ch'in would be defeated by Hu (胡) and the Emperor immediately ordered General Meng T'ien (蒙恬) to dispatch an army of 300,000 men to resist the Hsiung-nu, or Hu. He also ordered the building of the Great Wall as a defense against Hu. This is an example of the political power and influence which alchemists wielded over Emperors and Kings for many generations.

Up to the time of the Han Dynasty alchemy was widely practiced and believed in. Alchemists in those days employed many kinds of magical arts, such as the "art of yellow and white"—transmutation of baser metals into gold or silver—fasting for long periods, exorcism, divination, etc. They also professed to see emanations from the human body, invisible to ordinary people, and from these gaseous emanations to tell the fortune of the individual.

Of the emperors of the Han Dynasty, Wu Ti (140–88 B.C.) was most interested in alchemy, so alchemists came to call on him to offer their arts. One of them, Li Shao-chün (李少君) memorialized the Emperor, stating: [*Shih chi* 28.21].

If you will offer sacrifices to the Kitchen God, you will be able to change *tan sha* (丹砂)—cinnabar—into gold. When gold has been produced, you may make of it utensils for use in eating and drinking. Through using them, your life will be prolonged, so that you may see the blessed immortals of the isles of P'eng-lai, which lies in the midst of the ocean. After seeing them, you may go to T'ai-shan to offer sacrifice, then you will be immortal. These things were done by the Yellow Emperor. When I went to the isle, I saw An Ch'i-sheng (安期生) eating a large date, as big as a melon. He was an immortal living in P'eng-lai and he would come out to see the people if it pleased him to do so, otherwise he would not.

So the Emperor began to sacrifice to the Kitchen God and
sent alchemists abroad to find P'eng-lai and An Ch'i-sheng.
He also proposed to convert *tan sha* and other minerals into
gold. Later Li Shao-chün and other alchemists became
prominent and were held in honor on account of their study
of alchemy.

At the end of the later Han Dynasty, there was a native
of P'ei (沛縣) in Anhui province by the name of Chang Tao-
ling (張道陵)—a descendant in the ninth generation of Chang
Liang (張良)—who had a good knowledge of the classics and
secrets of astronomy, geography, charts, etc. Having become a great scholar at that time, he went to and fro between
the provinces of Kiangsu and Chekiang and had more than
one thousand disciples. Considering that honor and fame
offered no benefit to either health or mind, he attempted
to study immortality and the curing of diseases. He declared
that he had received secret instruction from an immortal—
T'ai Shang Lao Chün (太上老君), which gave him power to
dispel devils and to cure diseases by charms. By this means,
he could deceive fools, so his doctrine was very popular and
he went by the name of Chang T'ien-shih (天師) and twenty-
four chapters of a Taoist book were written by him. His
doctrine is said to have been handed down for nearly two
milleniums to the present day.

Alchemy was highly developed in the dynasties of Wei
(A.D. 220–264) and Chin (A.D. 265–419). During the second
century A.D., there was a native of Kiangsu named Wei Po-
yang (魏伯陽). He was a Taoist and well educated. He
wrote a book entitled *Chou yi ts'an t'ung ch'i* (周易參同契)
describing the interesting mystery of alchemy. It is regarded
as the oldest work known on the secret of compounding the
"Elixir of Life." Once upon a time, the legend goes, Wei
went with his three disciples to a mountain to engage in
the preparation of pills. After their preparation, he tried
them first on a dog and the dog died, then he took some him-

self and he died too. And when one of his disciples took
them, he also fell down to the ground. Then the other two
disciples said to each other: "What is the use of taking
such a pill to get immortality when it makes people die after
taking it?" So they left the mountain together. But Wei
Po-yang jumped up and put some more of the pills into the
mouths of his disciple and the dog. After a little while, they
both got up and became immortal!

During the reign of the Emperor Yüan (A.D. 317–322)
of the Chin Dynasty, there was a famous Taoist and alchemist, named Ko Hung (葛洪) (about A.D. 281–361), with
the pseudonym of Pao-p'u tzu (抱朴子), who wrote a book
with the same title. Although he was poor he desired to
study. He chopped wood in exchange for paper or pen, and
read and copied all books that he could borrow. Then he
became a great scholar, but he refused to be an official and
devoted himself to historical and other old books. His
teacher, Cheng Ssu-yüan (鄭思遠) said to him: "My teacher
Ko Hsien-weng (葛仙翁) stated that he ought to teach those
who were able to study his doctrine. Now you are the
grandson of Ko Hsien-weng, so I shall teach you what I have
received from my teacher."

After Ko Hung had inherited his teacher's learning, he
retired to Lo-fu Mountain (羅浮) in Kwangtung province to
practice magical arts and write his texts.

In *Pao-p'u tzu* he discussed alchemy and the preparation of drugs very fully and also dealt with the basic principles of the changes of universal things. Ko Hung suggested
various facts as evidence. He said: "Lead is white in color
but it may become red and vice versa" (16.2a). If we explain this by using modern chemical terms, it means that
white metallic lead may change into red lead, and vice versa.
Thus the Chinese understood such a reaction more than one
thousand years ago; but Ko Hung, it is suggested, probably
confused red lead with cinnabar.

He also said:

Cloud, rain, frost, and snow, all are naturally formed in the universe but they may be formed from chemicals and the products are the same as natural ones. With reference to birds, animals, and insects, their form is made by Creation, but it may sometimes be metamorphosed. The nature of human beings is the most spiritual one but men and women may change into the appearance of cranes, stones, tigers, monkeys, sand, turtles, etc. Furthermore, a mountain can be changed into an abyss and a valley into a hill. Change then is a natural phenomenon, so it will not be wondered at that gold and silver can be made from other substances. Some people of meager knowledge and experience usually regard as untrue all unexpected and mysterious changes which were neither mentioned by the Duke of Chou and Confucius nor recorded in the old books. How ignorant they are! (16.2a–2b.)

In the chapter entitled *Chin tan p'ien* (金丹篇) in the *Pao-p'u tzu* (4.2b) Ko Hung also dealt with the "elixir of life" in detail:

According to the instructions of Lao tzu, you will suffer distress if you have not obtained any elixir (還丹) and *chin yeh* (金液)—golden liquid. Grains support the lives of the people. Men must depend upon them for living and will die without them. Is the spiritual drug not ten thousand times more beneficial than grains? The longer gold and elixir are subjected to the action of fire, the more they pass through remarkable transformations. Gold, when it is melted, can never be destroyed, even after being heated hundreds of times, nor can it become corroded, if buried under the earth however long. By taking these two substances and by training their bodies people enable themselves to remain young and never die.

Again, Ko Hung advised the people to seek for immortality, in the following words (4.4a–5a):

The well-to-do people will not pay attention to the works of Confucius and Mo tzu, nor improve moral conditions, but will only spend their time selfishly or uselessly. What some do is either for glory or for riches and others waste their time in traveling, drinking, sexual pleasure, music, dressing, archery, gambling, playing chess, etc. When they have an opportunity of hearing the doctrines of Taoism explained they seem drunk or sleepy even in the daytime. They do not try to discover the secret of immortality but ruin their lives in dissipation. Those who know it will keep the secret and understand that they need not ask for anything from others. How can they be compelled to disclose the secret? There is a common saying that if long life could have been attained, the ancient rich and honorable folk would certainly have attained it, but, as they did not, there could not have been any such thing. But the wealthy and honored of old were exactly the same as those of the present: how could they attain this immortality if they did not believe in it and seek it, but cared only for the gratification of their present desires? Even if people can not believe that life can be prolonged and immortality attained, it is worth a trial. In case some trifling effect is gained by the trial—even to living two or three centuries—would this not be better than the common short life of man? The arts of Taoism are harder to understand than any other thing in the world. How can our common thought decide that there is no way of prolonging life? If it is claimed that there is no such thing because ordinary folk do not believe it, are the wise very numerous among ordinary folk? If some should know the ideas of Taoism and through the practices seek for immortality, are they really perfect fools and inferior to others? Some are suspicious and fear that they would be ridiculed by the others and considered stupid if immortality is not acquired. But if, ratiocination failing the once in ten thousand times, there really should be such a way to immortality, would it not be their turn to be ridiculed by the obtainers thereof.

Alchemy was still popular up to the T'ang Dynasty (A.D. 618–907) and Sung Dynasty (A.D. 960–1279). During the period of the T'ang Dynasty many emperors, such as Jui-tsung (睿宗) (A.D. 681–689), Hsüan-tsung (A.D. 713–755), and Hsien-tsung (憲) (A.D. 806–820), were friendly with the alchemists. It is stated in the Old History of the T'ang Dynasty (15.33) that during the 14th year of Yüan-ho (A.D. 819), P'ei Ling, (裴潾) a minister, memorialized the Emperor Hsien-tsung concerning the alchemists. He said:

Since last year, a great many alchemists have been introduced to the Court. If there were real immortals they would hide themselves in the mountains and be afraid of being known to the people.

Those who have waited upon the families of honorable persons, offering their strange magic, merely for the purpose of benefiting themselves—how can we believe in them and take their drugs? Drugs are used for curing diseases and not for daily food. We human beings, of course, should not injure our stomach and intestine by taking such metallic, earthy, and poisonous substances which have been heated over a fire. In ancient times, when the Emperor wanted to take medicine his minister had to try it first. Now the man who offers it should take it himself first for one year, then it may be proved whether it is good or not.

During this time there was a famous Taoist or alchemist named Lü Yen (呂巖) who was greatly honored by the people and his pseudonum Ch'un-yang (純陽)—Pure Positive—was well known. He wanted to be quiet and did not think of glory and honor. Later he followed a teacher to study methods of curing sick people and the transmutation of metals by the secret art of "yellow and white." He published many Taoist books.

Chang Po-tuan (張伯端) or Tzu-yang (紫陽) (A.D. 1075) was another famous alchemist of that time. He also studied the art of preparing the elixir and wrote a book entitled *Wu chen p'ien* (悟眞篇)—Essays on Alchemy—containing eighty-one chapters, discussing the mystery of the "inner" and "outer" elixir (內丹外丹), the "Esoteric and exoteric drug."

At the beginning of the Sung Dynasty, there was a Taoist by the name of Ch'en T'uan (陳搏) who went to the mountain to study alchemical arts. He refused to accept an official position which the Emperor T'ai-tsu (A.D. 960–976) had offered him, but lived quietly trying to discover the secret of how to prepare the elixir.

After the Yüan Dynasty (A.D. 1279–1368), Chinese Alchemy seemed to fall into disrepute, but a valuable alchemical book—*Chin tan ta yao* (金丹大要), "Grand Essentials of the Elixir of Life"—was published at the end of that Dynasty, constituting an important contribution to alchemy. Ch'en Chih-hsü (陳致虛), the author of this book, had studied the secret of preparing elixirs, and ten chapters of the book were written by his hand. After his work was completely finished, he realized that the people would not clearly understand his meaning unless verbal teaching was given. For this purpose he took his book and traveled to the south, extending his journey to the east and the west of the Yang-tzu River and instructed more than one hundred disciples. He also wrote a great number of commentaries on various kinds of alchemical books. During the dynasties of Ming (A.D. 1368–1644) and Ch'ing (A.D. 1644–1912) Chinese Alchemy appears to have been completely abandoned but we must admit that there may have been many alchemists working in the mountains, unknown to the people.

METHODS OF PREPARATION OF *CHIN TAN*

Chin tan, an alchemical term in Chinese, first appearing in *Pao-p'u tzu*, comes to refer to a drug or elixir which was prepared by the alchemists for prolonging life and transmuting metals. It reminds us of the "Philosopher's Stone" in western Alchemy because the latter was considered to have the same effect as *chin tan*. In the *Pao-p'u tzu*, however, the term is to be translated "gold and/or elixir."

Ingredients—What *chin tan* was and how to prepare it has attracted the attention of historians of chemistry and modern chemists who are interested in the study of Chinese Alchemy. The language of the ancient alchemists is very hard to understand. It is supposed by some that *chin tan* may have consisted of mercury, sulfur, lead, etc., a compound or mixture prepared in accordance with a theory not unlike that of Geber who supposed that every metal contained mercury and sulfur.

Both lead and mercury were discovered and used at a very early date in China, the former probably earlier than the latter. Wei Po-yang, a great alchemist, had studied them.

He knew (ch. 1.22) that white lead might be reduced to
metallic lead when it was heated over a fire and that mercury, which occurs in *tan sha*—cinnabar—might be distilled
out and solidified by the addition of sulfur. He also suggested (2.14, 15, 18, 19) that the combination of lead and
mercury is like a fight between a dragon and a tiger.

Chin tan ta yao 5.2–4 (*Tao tsang* 736) states that
tan sha, sulfur, and mercury are the three principal materials
used in preparing the elixir. Hence, we come to the conclusion that *chin tan* may have consisted of impure mercuric
sulfide.

Further reference to the ingredients of *chin tan* may be
found in another alchemical book entitled *Huang pai ching*
(黃白鏡), a book of the Ming Dynasty, describing the method
of the transmutation of metals. It specifies (5.1) that *chu
sha* (硃砂) (another name for *tan sha*) viz., cinnabar, and lead
are needed for making the elixir, and that a pill in the shape
of a pearl or a grain of rice is formed and found in the lead,
after mixing and heating these two ingredients. It is also
noted (7.2) that sulfur is the active principle of *chu sha*.

As regards the theory of the reaction, the same book explains (8.2) that the sulfur differs from sand and stone in
being the "real spirit" (眞一之氣) contained in lead. Originally, there was no such "spirit" in lead, but after mixing
and heating it with *chu sha* a little of the "divine fire" (神火)
contained in it makes its way into the lead and a piece of rice-
like pearl is thus formed. This is sulfur. If it could be
drawn out by heating, it would be a kind of mysterious drug
for solidifying mercury. It is also a similar interpretation
(9.2) that a small amount of the third of the Five Elements—
water—contained in lead is needed to make sulfur active.
When sulfur is allowed to act upon mercury, a piece of "pure
yang"—i.e., dry metal—is obtained.

According to recent knowledge, decomposition of mercuric sulfide and amalgamation of mercury and lead may

take place when the foregoing materials are mixed and
heated, but the ancients did not know this and so the meta-
phors of *"yin"* and *"yang"* and *"wu hsing"* as above mentioned were taken for an explanation.

Furthermore, Ko Hung considered that *tan sha* could
give people immortality. He said (4.3b):

> After grass and wood have been burnt, they become ashes,
> but *tan sha* can be changed into mercury by heating over a fire,
> and vice versa. It is far different from the ordinary vegetable sub-
> stance, so it can make people immortal.

The other term *chu sha* appears in the Chinese Materia
Medica which describes how it may be taken for prolonging
life and curing many kinds of disease. Thus, it is clear that
chin tan, *tan sha*, and *chu sha* are the same thing—mercuric
sulfide—under different names.

The alchemists also claimed that this substance could
be changed into gold or silver which might then be eaten in
order to attain immortality. This, of course, cannot be believed, but we may suppose that some ore of gold or silver
was added to the materials at the times of preparation and,
after heating, the noble metal was isolated. It is also considered that the ancients always regarded *tan sha*, orpiment, sulfur, etc., as "gold" (see *Pao tsang lun* (寶藏論),
quoted in Materia Medica 8.1 and 5) and that the definitions
of gold and silver in ancient times may not have been so
strict or definite as those of the present day.

Apparatus—The apparatus used by the ancient alchemists as described in various Taoist books consisted of
three kinds—oven or furnace, crucible or container, and
distilling apparatus.

1.   Oven or furnace—This was used for heating the materials for the elixir, which were placed in a container or crucible. The crucible was put inside the oven and surrounded
completely or partially with suitable fuel which was then
ignited.

The types of the oven in use were many and varied. One kind is shown in Figure 2, consisting of a stove with a flat top, in the center of which was a hole for the introduction of the crucible and emission of flame. The diameter of the middle portion was about one foot and three inches, and the circumference of the flat top was one foot and six inches. Another kind was constructed with a grating of twelve or thirteen iron rods one foot and three inches long and $5/8$ inch thick at the bottom, and supported about three inches above the ground on legs to allow air to pass upward through the fire.

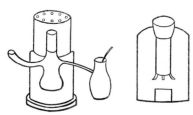

Figure 3.   Alchemist's furnaces, two kinds, containing water-cooled areas. (Tao tsang 588.2, p. 9)

Figure 2.   An alchemist's furnace.

According to *Tan fang hsü chih* (丹房湏知), (*Tao tsang* 588, p. 9), a book of A.D. 1163, the oven was divided into upper and lower sections. There were two types. In the first type, the upper or fire section held the container and fuel and had a perforated top. In the lower section was mounted a water vessel packed in ashes and mud. A tube passing through this vessel allowed water to be introduced when desired and also served as an outlet for steam. The crucible was in contact with the water container at the junction between the upper and lower sections of the oven. In the second type the fire section was the lower part while the upper part contained water. Thus in both types a small area of the reaction vessel—container or crucible—could be

kept cooled during the heating. The two types are shown
in Figure 3. Two other examples of the first type are also
shown in Figures 4 and 5, the former is found in a book published sometime after the T'ang Dynasty (ended A.D. 907)
and the latter in a book of A.D. 1225.

2. *Container or crucible*—This was generally called, in
the Taoist books, *"ting"* (鼎)—cauldron—and was of two
kinds. The one above mentioned was the "fire crucible,"
containing the necessary materials and surrounded com-

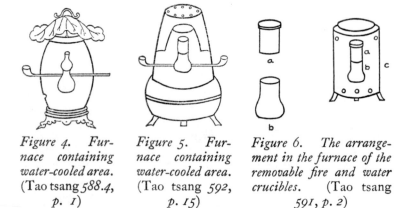

Figure 4. Fur-
nace containing
water-cooled area.
(Tao tsang 588.4,
p. 1)

Figure 5. Fur-
nace containing
water-cooled area.
(Tao tsang 592,
p. 15)

Figure 6. The arrange-
ment in the furnace of the
removable fire and water
crucibles. (Tao tsang
591, p. 2)

pletely or partially by the fire; the other was the "water
crucible," sometimes called "water jar," which has also been
described in the preceding paragraph, being used simply as
a cooler in order to prevent over-heating of the fire crucible.
On account of this fact, the Taoist books always speak of
them as "Heaven and Earth" or *"Yin* and *Yang,"* male and
female.

Both of these crucibles are shown in Figure 6, in which
(*a*) is the fire crucible with a stone cover and (*b*) is the water
crucible of porcelain holding about three liters of water.

The mouth of the water crucible should fit with the bottom of the fire crucible so that they may be placed one above the other in the oven (c) as shown in the figure. The oven used in this case is made of earth or earthenware, two feet and nine inches high, one foot and five inches in diameter with two holes at the upper part and three holes at the bottom.

Another example of these crucibles is shown in Figure 7. It consisted of a jar half-filled with water and covered with a round piece of brick having a hole through its center.

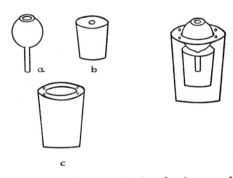

Figure 7. The water crucible and lower part of the furnace are packed in earth while the fire and fire crucible are above ground. (Tao tsang *591, p. 6*)

Figure 8. Furnace having fitted parts of silver and gold. (Tao tsang *592, p. 8*)

The reaction vessel—fire crucible—was placed on the brick and over the hole. The water jar and brick were packed in moist earth while the fire, as usual, surrounded the fire crucible. The whole apparatus was enclosed in an oven as illustrated.

When a larger cooling surface was required the "water lake" (水海) was always used instead of the "water jar." This consisted of a water container placed also above the fire crucible and usually sealed into its mouth in order to cool its upper part. In order to increase the cooling surface, a

straight or coiled tube was extended from the bottom of the
"water lake" into the fire crucible.

In Figure 8, reprinted from a book of A.D. 1225—*Chin
hua ch'ung pi tan ching pi chih* (金華沖碧丹經祕旨)—(*a*)
is a "water lake" made of silver, and was capable of holding
half a catty of water. The lower tube which projected from
it was of red gold and had a length of about four inches and
weighed about one tael. The reaction chamber (*b*) was also
made of red gold and had a weight of from one-half to one
catty. The golden tube projecting from the bottom of (*a*)

*Figure 9. Fur-
nace contrived for
greater heating
surface.* (Tao
tsang *592*, p. *4*)

*Figure 10. Device for greater
heating surface.* (Tao tsang *592*,
pp. *5, 6*)

passed through the hole at the center of the top of (*b*), and
then the reaction chamber together with the "water lake"
was placed in a porcelain vessel (*c*) which had been plastered
with "six-one mud" and was used as an oven. All the con-
necting parts were closely fitted and tightly sealed with
plaster or mud. They were allowed to dry before heating in
the oven.

There were still other forms in use but a more complicated one with several semi-circular pipes for increasing the
heating surface is shown in Figure 9, which is reproduced
from the same book. The same book also recommends the

jacketed crucible, shown in Figure 10 in which (*a*) is the "water lake" made of silver with a hole at its bottom and (*b*) is a jacketed crucible—fire crucible—with a straight pipe to fit into the hole at the bottom of (*a*). Both are connected and placed in the oven (*c*) as shown in the figure.

The various crucibles were made of gold, silver, copper, iron, or earthenware.

3. Distilling apparatus—This apparatus was used chiefly for the preparation of mercury from *tan sha*—cinnabar. Figure 11 shows a very simple form of still which con-

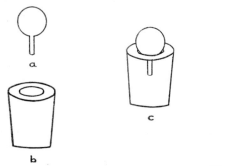

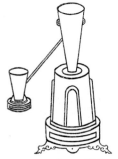

Figure 11. Apparatus for preparing mercury from cinnabar.
(Tao tsang *592, p. 4*)

Figure 12. An efficient still with still-head and air condenser.
(Tao tsang *588.2, p. 7*)

sisted of a short-necked, round-bottom porcelain flask (*a*) having a capacity of one and a half liters of water. When used it was filled with the proper amount of cinnabar and other materials and its mouth was closed with pieces of porcelain. Then it was inverted and set in a jar (*b*), neck downward, so that it sealed the circular mouth of the latter (*c*). The bottom of the jar was filled with water to a depth of $1/4$ inch. The flask was heated in an oven, whereupon mercury vaporized out of the flask and condensed in the water in the jar.

A more efficient apparatus, pictured in *Tan fang hsü chih* (p. 7) consisted of a still with its head projecting from the oven and from this an air condenser leading to a receiver, as shown in Figure 12.

Processes—Ko Hung in his book *Pao-p'u tzu* (4.5b–7a) described methods for the preparation of nine kinds of elixir —*tan*. The first one was prepared by heating *hsüan huang* for thirty-six days after having sealed it with "six-one mud" which had been prepared by mixing several tens of catties of common salt, magnesium chloride, alum, oyster shell, *ch'ih shih chih* (赤石脂)—a kind of clay, red in color, containing ferric oxide—talc, and white lead with orpiment liquor and alum solution.

If twenty taels of this elixir, according to *Pao-p'u tzu*, were mixed with one hundred catties of mercury and heated over the fire, yellow gold would be produced. Otherwise, this process should be repeated.

The orpiment liquor was prepared by putting one catty of orpiment and two taels of niter into a bamboo pipe which was then sealed and immersed in vinegar and buried under the ground to the depth of three feet. After twenty days a complete solution would result.

It seems to the writer that a mixture of sulfides, chiefly mercuric sulfide, may have been formed in the second of the above-mentioned processes.

Sublimation was also carried out by the ancient alchemists for preparing *tan*. For instance, a certain kind of elixir was prepared by heating orpiment and realgar and covering them with a brass vessel in which some vinegar was put. After one hundred days a red colored product was formed. It was said that people could prolong their life if they ate it.

Gold in the solid form might be made into a liquid one by digesting it in oil, wine, or vinegar in order to serve for drinking instead of eating.

THE "ART OF YELLOW AND WHITE"

In Chinese alchemy the so-called "art of yellow and white" furnished a method of transmuting the baser metals into gold or silver. With regard to this, three stories are given in *Pao-p'u tzu* as follows:

The first one (16.2b):

An educated official Wu Ta-wen (吳大文) stated that he saw Li Ken (李根), a Taoist, simmer lead and tin, and put a piece of another substance the size of a bean into the cauldron and mingle them with an iron spoon. Then they became silver after cooling. Wu Ta-wen had obtained the secret and intended to try it out by himself after fasting for a hundred days, but he did not succeed on account of remaining in office, so he always sighed and said that there was nothing interesting in the world.

The second one (16.3a):

Ch'eng Wei (程偉), an official of the Han Dynasty, liked the "art of yellow and white." He married a wife from an alchemist's family. He generally followed the Emperor out but grieved because he had no fashionable clothes. In order to serve his necessity, his wife obtained two pieces of satin by magic. Previously, he had failed to produce gold by following the recipe of an alchemical book. When his wife went to see him, he was just fanning the fire and heating a tube in which was some mercury. His wife told him that she would show him something. Then she took a small quantity of some substance from a wallet and sprinkled it into the mercury. After a little while, it became silver.

The third one (16.3b):

Hua Ling-ssu (華令思), a former prefect of Lu-chiang (蘆江), was a highly educated scholar. He did not believe anything which was not right, but he once ordered a Taoist to try the "art of yellow and white" when he had heard something about it from him. The Taoist melted lead with the addition of something else in an iron vessel to form silver, which in turn was heated with another unknown substance to make gold.

From the foregoing narratives it would appear that lead, tin, and mercury were used in this art and that these metals, by the action of some chemicals added by the alchemists, may have been changed into other substances which had properties like those of silver or gold.

Further reference to methods of transmutation of metals may be found in the same book. One of them (16.7a–7b) consisted in taking not less than five catties of orpiment, produced from Wu-tu (武都), "as red as a cock's comb, shining and containing no impurities," pounding it into powder and mixing it with the gallbladder of a cow. The mixture was roasted so as to make it as dry as red earth. Into a 10-liter vessel common salt and copper sulfate powder were first put to the thickness of $1/2$ inch, then the powdered orpiment to about $3/4$ inch, above which common salt was placed again. The vessel was filled with successive layers like this, with a final three-inch layer of pieces of charcoal as big as the stone of a date. The outside of the vessel was plastered with common salt mixed with mud, and then covered with an inverted vessel also plastered till there was no leakage. This was kept dry in the shade for one month and then heated for three days and nights over a fire of horse dung.

Then the molten copper, it was said, might be blown out as in the case of smelting copper or iron. From this copper a vessel was cast. When this vessel was ready, it was filled with *tan sha* liquor and covered and heated again over the fire of horse dung. The method of preparing *tan sha* liquor was similar to that of preparing orpiment liquor as described in a preceding paragraph. After thirty days it was said that gold was obtained. In the same way, a vessel was made out of this gold and filled with *tan sha* liquor and heated over the same fire again for thirty days. After taking this out, it was pounded and remelted. Two parts of it were mixed with one part of raw cinnabar and some mercury so

*Figure 13. Alchemists at work in their mountain laboratory. Fur-
naces and other chemical equipment are shown as well as a mirror
hanging above a furnace, a sword, and other magical apparatus.*

as to make them into "yellow gold" of a brilliant color suitable for making nails.

Another example of these methods (16.7b–8a) was to take a piece of tin plate, nine inches square and $1^3/_4$ inches thick, to be daubed with mud consisting of red salt (impure gypsum) and lime water and put into an earthenware vessel made of red earth. It was covered and sealed and heated over a fire of horse dung for thirty days. When opened, the contents had the appearance of ashes in which were found some small solid pieces of the size of a bean which were called "yellow gold" by the alchemists.

A simpler method recommended by Ko Hung (16.8b) consisted of putting alum into an iron vessel and heating it to froth over a charcoal fire. Then such quantity of mercury as desired was added, and stirred uniformly, the heating being continued. On pouring the heated mixture upon the ground, a silvery product was formed. In a vessel one part each of *tan sha* liquor and *ts'eng ch'ing* blue—a kind of mineral containing cobalt—liquor (曾青水) and two parts of orpiment liquor were mixed and boiled together over a mild fire. They were stirred a few times so as to mix them well and then put over the charcoal fire again in order to bring them to boil. Some of the above silvery product was added and boiled again. On pouring out onto the ground it became "purple gold" of the best color.

Apparently, the products obtained from the processes described above were mixtures or alloys which had the appearance of gold or silver.

Chapter 3—METALS

ALTHOUGH, as elsewhere, the use of copper began early in China, there was no proper term given to it in ancient times. The word for "gold," "*chin*" (金), appearing in old literature represents not only gold but also such metals as silver, copper, etc.

Because of the more complicated process of smelting iron, it came into use later than copper and bronze, even though its ores were plentiful in China. The impure metal, perhaps of meteoric origin, was early brought into use.

Edward Thorp states in his "History of Chemistry" that the Chinese already knew the method of making steel and of tempering it before 2220 B.C., but according to recent investigations, the manufacture of steel began in the time of the Warring States (481–255 B.C.).

After the First Emperor had collected copper weapons for casting twelve colossal statues (about 213 B.C.), iron was largely used instead of copper, although very many copper objects were still cast and fabricated in the Han Dynasty; such as mirrors, lamps, stoves, etc., some of them being still in existence. It is then concluded that the dynasties of Ch'in and Han may be considered as a period between the age of copper and that of iron.

Lead was known when the practice of alchemy began and tin was used at an early time for making bronze, but the ancient Chinese did not know how to distinguish them.

The discovery of zinc was later than that of the above-mentioned metals. J. W. Mellor states in his "Treatise on

Chemistry" that the method of preparing zinc originated in India from where it was introduced into China, but he also states in his "Inorganic Chemistry" that zinc was brought from China and the East Indies under the name "tutanego" in the sixteenth century. Holmes says in his "General Chemistry" that the Chinese isolated the element in the sixteenth century but Europe made no progress with it until the eighteenth century. It is also said that the art of preparing zinc was introduced into Europe from China by the Portuguese at the beginning of the eighteenth century.

F. C. Chang (章鴻釗), has proved, by investigation and analysis, that the use of zinc began in 9–22 A.D., and that its development might be divided into four periods.[1] The first period dates from the last of the Han Dynasty and down to the Sui (A.D. 589–618) and T'ang (A.D. 618–907) dynasties. During this period, the zinc contained in the articles was probably introduced from impure lead. The second period was the T'ang Dynasty; yü shih (鍮石)—i.e., brass, made from lu kan shih (爐甘石), i.e., smithsonite, $ZnCO_3$— was used for making ornaments in which zinc was the chief component, but the Chinese did not know about it at that time. The third period was from the Sung to the beginning of the Ming Dynasty. Lu kan shih was mixed with copper in order to make brass coins. As the result of this addition, the proportion of zinc contained in them was increased, but the Chinese as yet did not understand how to isolate it. The fourth period dates from the middle of the Ming Dynasty; zinc and brass were prepared from lu kan shih and also metallic zinc was used for making coins or other articles.

The name of antimony does not occur in ancient Chinese literature although the present production of this material in China is very considerable. It has been shown by analysis that certain wares of not very ancient times contain small amounts of it.

---

[1] *Journal of Science* (written in Chinese), Vol. 8, 233–43 and Vol. 9, 1116–27.

It is interesting to notice the ancient Chinese conceptions of the source of metals. Some might have believed that they originated independently and were not related to one another. But it is stated in various ancient books that they are supposed to have had the same origin. For instance, lead is regarded as the ancestor of all metals, having the property of controlling various kinds of metal or mineral, and that it is the ancestor of gold, silver, copper, and tin because it is always found in the ores of these metals as mentioned in the Chinese Materia Medica 8.4. Another assumption was similar to the phlogiston theory of the Europeans that the metallic compound was to be regarded as the "essence" of the metal, just as copper green (verdigris) was called the "essence" of copper, so with lead frost (lead acetate) (see the Chinese Materia Medica 8.4).

According to the development of the knowledge of metals, alloys were made in order to produce metals better suited to various uses. The invention of alloys was almost as early as the discovery of copper because the latter was rarely used in a pure state on account of its being too soft for making articles. We must admit that there were several kinds of copper alloy in ancient times. It is stated in *T'ien kung k'ai wu*, that when copper is mixed with *lu kan shih*—zinc ore—brass of a golden color is formed; with arsenic, white copper; with alum, blue copper; and with tin, bronze is produced. The last is assumed to be the alloy which was prepared and used in the earliest times, and its composition, properties, and uses are stated in detail in *K'ao kung chi* (考工記 40.4b) as follows:

There are six kinds of *ch'i* (齊)—i.e., alloys—those containing five parts of metal and one part of tin are used for making tripods and bells; four parts of metal and one part of tin, for axes; three parts of metal and one part of tin for spears and lances; two parts of metal and one part of tin for larger knives; four parts of metal and two parts of tin for smaller knives and arrows; one part of metal and one part of tin for mirrors.

Figure 14.   Bronze objects of the Shang and Chou dynasties.

Figure 15. Bronze pieces of the Shang and Chou dynasties.

This short description shows that the art of making alloys had been studied carefully by the Chinese ancients. Although only metal and tin are mentioned in this quotation, we must remember that the word "metal" may stand for gold, copper, or iron, and "tin" for lead and others in ancient Chinese literature.

Hence the proportion of *ch'i* may be calculated and tabulated as follows:

	ch'i	Metal, % (including Au, Ag, Cu, and Fe)	Tin, % (including Sn, Pb, etc.)
1.	For bells and tripods	Below 83.33	Above 16.67
2.	For axes	Below 80.00	Above 20.00
3.	For spears and lances	Below 75.00	Above 25.00
4.	For larger knives	Below 66.67	Above 33.33
5.	For smaller knives and arrows	Below 67.00	Above 33.00
6.	For mirrors	Below 50.00	Above 50.00

In order to carry out further investigation, analytical work was done by Dr. Chikashige and T. Liang (梁津), affording a great contribution to those who are interested in the study of Chinese ancient metallic wares. The former investigator stated after collecting his analytical data that the composition of the bronze wares produced before the T'ang Dynasty is like that recorded in *K'ao kung chi* but those after the Sung Dynasty contain less tin. The analytical results are given below:

Percentage of Tin Contained in Ancient Bronze Objects.

		Found by analysis	According to literature
1.	Bell	19%	17%
2.	Axe	13–17%	20%
3.	Spear and lance	16–22%	25%
4.	Large knives	...	33%
5.	Small knives and arrows	...	33%
6.	Mirror	26–31%	50%

Various specimens of the ancient wares of the Chou Dynasty were analyzed by T. Liang and were reported to differ not more than 5% from those recorded in *K'ao kung chi*.

Referring to the suitable temperature to be used and the color of the flame appearing in the process of smelting metals, the same book gives the following descriptions (40.7b–8b):

> When the family of Li (栗氏) made the volumetric vessels, if the "gold" (including copper and iron) and "tin" (including lead) were pure, the vessels would not decrease in quantity during the time of remelting. . . . At first, the black and impure gas was completely expelled from the molten gold and tin, next in order the yellowish white, bluish white, and blue gas, and finally it was ready to be used for casting."

The commentary added by Tu Mu (杜牧)—a literatus or poet of the T'ang Dynasty—states that remelting was a process of refining to which "gold" and "tin" should be subjected until there was no more decrease in weight so as to make them fine and durable. To use "gold" (i.e., copper, etc.) for making articles, "tin" should be mixed with it. At the beginning of the process of remelting, there were many impurities which made the color of the flame black; when they were gotten rid of, the flame would turn yellow but yet not be clean. After refining for a longer time the molten metal should have a flame of a bluish white color, leaving some substance floating on the surface. When the white color had disappeared and became purely blue, the alloy had attained the highest degree of purity and was suitable for casting.

We can thus be sure that the Chinese early had much experience in adjusting the temperature of refining metals by observations on the color of the flame. Their methods agree with the principles of present-day blow-pipe assaying.

Again, Hamada Kosaku (濱田耕作) has stated that the addition of tin to copper for making bronze for the purpose

Figure 16. A bronze ting (*tripod, furnace, or incense burner*) *of the Shang Dynasty.*

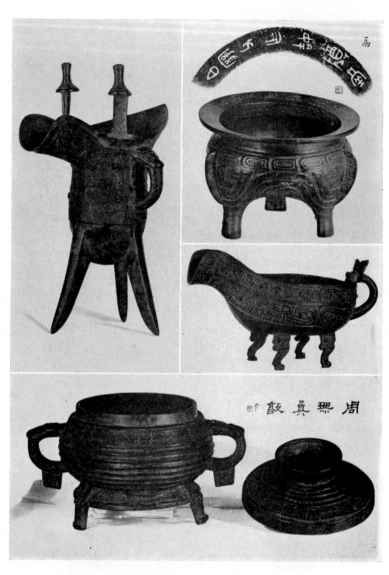

Figure 17.   Bronzes of the Chou Dynasty.

of increasing its hardness was probably started in a certain locality and introduced from there to others. The percentage of tin contained in bronze has varied according to the age producing it. About three thousand years before the Christian era, the Egyptians and Babylonians had used bronze. But it is said that the bronze age in China dates from a time prior to the former Han Dynasty (206 B.C.– A.D. 23) or between the dynasties of Shang (before 1100 B.C.) and Chou (1122–255 B.C.). During those times, many elegant and beautiful tripods and other vessels were produced, and some of them are still in existence, as shown in Figures 14, 15, 16, and 17.

The coins of the Han Dynasty were cast from an alloy of more complicated composition. It is stated in *Han shu* 24 B.21 (漢書)—the History of the Han Dynasty—that all the valuable articles as well as coins were cast with copper mixed with tin and *lien* (連). By investigation and analysis, F. C. Chang has proved that zinc was called *lien* in ancient times.[2] Thus brass was probably invented and has been used since those times. He also analyzed many samples of ancient coins of different periods and reported that they contain varying percentages of zinc. The composition of brass is clearly given in *T'ien kung k'ai wu* (published in A.D. 1637) and may now be tabulated as follows:

Brass	Cu, %	Zn, %
For coins and others	70	30
For wares of higher grade	60	40
For wares of lower grade	40	60

Further, according to the Chinese Materia Medica and other literature, lead and arsenic were also early known by the Chinese and were added to copper for making alloys.

---

[2] *Journal of Science*, Vol. 8, 233–43 and Vol. 9, 1116–27.

THE ANCIENT CHINESE METHODS OF METALLURGY
AND OF REFINING METALS

Although metals were used at an early time in China, yet the ancient methods of metallurgy were clumsy and are now obsolete. It was not until the period of Kuang-hsü (A.D. 1875–1908) of the Ch'ing Dynasty, that a great foundry was established at Han-yang in Hupeh province and that the modern scientific process was thence introduced into other parts of China.

The old methods are scarcely mentioned in Chinese literature, but a method of making steel in or before the eleventh century is roughly stated in a record of the Sung Dynasty (A.D. 960–1279) written by Shen Kua (沈括) (A.D. 1030–1094). He says (*Meng ch'i pi t'an* 3.6) that iron containing steel is similar to flour containing gluten. In order to get gluten, all starch contained in flour must be washed away and in the same way steel is made by refining iron over fire more than one hundred times and weighing it after each time until its weight is no longer decreased. Then pure steel is obtained. According to this we see that the method used was merely a process of getting rid of the impurities to as great an extent as possible, which almost agrees with the principle of the modern process.

Further, the methods of metallurgy and of refining metals in or before the seventeenth century are described in *T'ien kung k'ai wu* 14.1–3, of which the following is a brief sketch:

Gold—Gold occurred in ore and some was found in alluvial deposit in rivers. Different names were given to it. The ore or deposit should be washed first and then refined. After being refined in the furnace, the first product was light yellow in color, turning red when it was refined again.

For the purpose of adulteration, silver was frequently added to gold. They might be separated by beating into thin leaves and cutting into pieces which were then daubed with mud and put into an earthen crucible to be melted with the addition of borax. Silver would be absorbed by the

Figure 18. Smelting silver ore. The men operating the blower are protected by the brick wall from the heat of the fire.

earth, leaving gold in a pure state, and silver might be later withdrawn by putting lead into the crucible.

Silver—Before putting into the furnace (14.5) the ore should be selected and washed. The furnace was built of earth, in the shape of a large altar to the height of about five and a half feet, and the bottom was packed with fragments of porcelain and ashes of charcoal. Each furnace would hold two piculs of ore which was surrounded with two hundred catties of chestnutwood charcoal. Near the furnace,

a brick wall more than ten feet high was built up, at the rear
of which a blast bellows was placed to be operated by two or
three men, so that air might be blown into the furnace.
Men might work comfortably behind the wall which shel-

*Figure 19.   Refining of silver.   The workers watch the process closely
while protecting their faces with fans.*

tered them from the heat, as shown in Figure 18.   When the
charcoal had been exhausted some more was added by means
of an iron fork.   As soon as it was hot enough, the ore was
melted into a mass.   During this time, the silver and lead
formed an alloy.   From two piculs of ore, the yield was one
hundred catties of molten mass.   After being cooled, the
mass was taken out and put into a refining stove, called frog-
stove (Figure 19), which was filled with charcoal of pine
wood, leaving a small hole for the emission and observation

of the flame. The bellows or fan was also employed for blowing in air. As soon as the temperature was high enough, lead sank down in the form of litharge as "bottoms" which might be reduced into metallic lead in another stove. By means of lighted willow twigs, the operator could look from time to time through the hole into the stove. When lead was completely eliminated, precious silver was obtained.

When silver was intended for practical use, it could be adulterated only with copper and lead. To make powder or pieces into ingots of silver or to purify impure silver, the

Figure 20. Purification of impure silver.

process was carried out by mixing them with niter in a crucible which rested upon a tall furnace heated over a fire. That which sank down and adhered to the bottom of the crucible was called "rust of silver" (銀銹) and what was beaten out onto the ash pit was called "bottom of the furnace" (爐底). Then the "rust" and the "bottom" were put together into an earthen pot to be heated over the fire of a furnace (Figure 20). Lead fused first and overflowed from the pot. Copper might be separated from silver by means of iron rods.

Figure 22.   Smelting zinc ore.

Copper—Copper ore was washed first (14.12) to get rid of earth, sand, etc., before putting into the furnace (Figure 21 printed on the end papers of this book). After heating, copper in a fused state flowed out from the side of the furnace. If the ore used contained a large percentage of silver and lead, the metallurgical process was carried out in a furnace on the side of which were two holes one above the other. Lead fused first and flowed out from the upper hole and then copper from the lower one.

Zinc—Zinc was produced (14.13) from the ore *lu kan shih* (ZnCO₃). This mineral was put into earthen pots which were sealed tightly and dried slowly to prevent them from cracking when they were heated. Then these pots and cakes of charcoal were piled up in alternate layers, and wood was packed at the bottom to be fired at the same time in order to attain a red heat (Figure 22). The ore in the pots was thus fused into a mass which might be taken out after cooling and

breaking the pots. Zinc was obtained in this way with a
loss of 20%.

Iron—The iron minerals (14.15–16) known to the ancient people were only those which occurred on the surface
of the ground or not more than a few inches under it. They
were of two kinds—pieces and powder, and might be picked
up from the earth when ploughing with oxen (Figure 23).

After the prelimi-
nary treatment, the iron
mineral was melted in a
furnace which was built
of a mixture of salt and
mud. In most cases, it
rested on the side of a hill
but sometimes a large
wooden frame was con-
structed around it for
support. The work of
building was carried on
carefully; if any crack
occurred in the salted
mud, the whole work
would entirely fail. In
general, each furnace was
capable of holding two
thousand catties of min-
eral. Hard wood, coal,
or charcoal was used as

*Figure 23. Finding pieces of iron
ore when plowing.*

fuel according to convenience. Bellows were usually
operated by four or six men. After the mineral had partially
fused, molten iron flowed out from the hole opened at the
middle part of the furnace and previously sealed with mud.
It took six hours for working every day and about ten liters
of molten iron flowed out per hour. After each discharge,
air was blown in and the mineral was heated again.

Pig iron ready for refining and casting was thus produced in the form of long bars or round pieces which might be taken out from the molds for use.

To make wrought iron, a square basin was constructed at a place a few inches lower than the furnace and several feet distant from it, and at its side a short wall was also built up. Molten iron flowed out of the furnace and was led into

Figure 24. Metallurgy of iron. Blast furnace at right. Puddling at left.

the basin. Several men holding willow canes stood on the wall. Some damp mud was dried and then ground and sifted into flour-like powder. One man scattered quickly dried and powdered mud on to the molten iron, while the others stirred it by means of the willow canes. In this way, it was instantly converted into malleable iron, which, when moderately cooled, was either cut, in the basin, into square pieces or taken out to be beaten to make it into round pieces. These manipulations are shown in **Figure 24**.

The process of making steel consisted in mixing pig iron and wrought iron. The latter was beaten into thin sheets as broad as the finger and an inch and a half long. These sheets were tied up tightly, above them pig iron was put and then they were covered with broken straw which had previously been daubed with mud to prevent quick burning. The bottom of the bundles was daubed with mud as well. After putting into the furnace they were heated over a fire by blowing in air. As soon as the temperature was high enough, the pig iron fused first and gradually diffused into the wrought iron. When mixed uniformly, the material was taken out for hammering.

Figure 25. Tin ore smelted with the addition of lead.

Tin—There were two kinds of mineral (14.19–20) containing tin known in ancient times: the one was "mountain-tin" and the other "water-tin." The former was obtained from shallow mines but sometimes from the surface in mountain districts. The latter came out of the river, being black in color and in fine powder like sifted flour. Both of these were washed before smelting. A few hundred catties of mineral and the same weight of wood charcoal were fired in

a furnace. If the mineral did not fuse at the proper temperature, a small quantity of lead might be added in order
to ensure that the tin would flow out freely as shown in
Figure 25. Under the furnace was a pit packed with powdered charcoal and porcelain pieces, from which an iron pipe
was connected for running the molten tin into a lower pit at
the side of the furnace.

Lead—Lead produced from the mines (14.22) was more
abundant than copper and tin. There were three kinds of
lead. The first one came from the silver mines and occurred
with silver. After the first smelting, it was alloyed with
silver in the form of a mass which was then remelted to isolate it from the silver and to let it sink down to the bottom.
From this "bottom," lead was produced and known as
"lead of the silver-mine."

The second one was produced from the copper mine.
After the mineral was heated in the furnace, lead came out
first and then copper. This was called "lead of the copper
mine."

The third kind was obtained from the lead mine. After
the mineral was washed and smelted, the product, in a molten
state, was allowed to run through a long pipe into a long
earthen pit and was known as "lead of grass-knot" (草節鉛).

Beside the methods given in *T'ien kung k'ai wu* and outlined above, another method (*Sung shih* 180.21) of producing
copper was invented in the Sung Dynasty. It consisted in
dipping iron in a solution of blue vitriol (copper sulfate). It
is stated in the "History of the Sung Dynasty" that pig iron
is beaten into thin sheets which are put into a tank filled
with solution of blue vitriol for a few days. A red deposit
will form on the surface of the iron sheets and this deposit
may be scraped off to be melted three times in a furnace so
as to obtain pure copper. Approximately, two catties and
four taels of iron can yield one catty of copper. From the
viewpoint of modern knowledge, this method merely depends

upon the principal of displacement of metals in the electro-
motive series, but the ancient people did not understand this
and were astonished at seeing that iron might be converted
into copper in the solution of blue vitriol.

Mercury—Mercury was regarded as a kind of magic substance by the Chinese alchemists, and the method of its
preparation as well as its
properties were early in-
vestigated by them. To
prepare mercury a simple
process was carried out
by the roasting of cinna-
bar or the decomposition
of mercuric oxide. A
number of recipes for this
preparation from cinna-
bar are given in detail in
many alchemical books.
One method (*Tao tsang*
587, p. 1) consisted in
putting finely divided
cinnabar and roasted yel-
low vitriol $(Fe_2(SO_4)_3)$
powder in alternate layers
in a reaction chamber.
The surface of the in-
gredients was covered
with an inverted bottle

*Figure 26. Preparation of mer-
cury from cinnabar.*

and sealed with "six-one mud." Heating was then commenced, and it required about three days and three nights
before the oven might be opened and allowed to cool in order
to remove the liberated and sublimed mercury. A similar
method was given in the Chinese Materia Medica.

T'ien kung k'ai wu 16.41 also gives a process for sublimation. Cinnabar of an inferior quality or vermilion of

the second grade was mixed with water and rolled into bar-like pieces. Every thirty catties of these pieces required the same weight of charcoal for heating. They were heated in a furnace covered with an inverted vessel in the middle part of which was a small hole and the junction between the two was closely daubed with salted mud. At the top of the vessel was an iron condensing tube the outside of which was bound with hempen string and the connection also tightly sealed with salted mud. On firing, the condensing tube was connected with the vessel and its other end immersed in a jar filled with cold water as shown in Figure 26. After heating for ten hours, the powdered cinnabar or vermilion was competlely decomposed, the metallic mercury condensing on the inside of the jar. After cooling for one day, the product could be collected.

ANCIENT METHODS OF PREPARING CHEMICAL COMPOUNDS[3]

The study of the preparation of chemical compounds in China began at about the same time as iatrochemistry which, of course, commenced as early as an interest in alchemy. The *Pen ts'ao*—the Chinese Materia Medica—is said to have been compiled at a very early date even though it was not completed until the sixteenth century. It contains one hundred and thirty three kinds of inorganic medicines or minerals, the greater part of which are metallic compounds. Some of them occurred in nature and some were prepared artificially.

Wet methods were not common among the ancient workers. The products which they obtained were often impure because impure materials were always used and because proper methods of purification were not employed in those early times. Although the methods of preparation and identification as well as the properties of

---

[3] *Journal of Science*, Vol. 7, 675–83.

the metallic compounds prepared according to the description in the Chinese Materia Medica were interpreted philosophically rather than scientifically, yet the methods discovered by the skill of the ancient Chinese are worthy of mention. These may be described briefly as follows:

Compounds of gold and silver—Both gold and silver have little affinity for other elements, and therefore their salts were scarcely known to the ancient people. However, silver chloride and silver sulfide were prepared and used, the former is called "silver spangles" (銀屑) and the latter "black silver" (烏銀) in the Chinese Materia Medica.

Compounds of copper, iron, and tin—The compounds of copper produced in ancient times consisted of copper sulfate, copper carbonate, and copper acetate. The latter two were confused with each other and were designated by the single name of "copper green" (銅青). They were produced by the direct reaction of copper with moisture and carbon dioxide in the air and by the addition of vinegar to copper. Tannate of copper was always prepared from copper and gallnuts for its use in colors.

The compounds of iron known to the ancient Chinese were iron sulfate, iron acetate, iron tannate, iron oxide, and iron sulfide. The first and the last of these will be discussed in a later paragraph dealing with alums. Iron acetate was produced by the action of vinegar on iron sheets and was known as "essence of iron." Iron tannate was prepared by the reaction of iron and gallnuts. Iron oxide of many names such as iron flower, red stone, red earth, etc., either occurred in nature or was prepared.

Only one compound of tin, namely, tin oxide, was known in ancient times. It was produced by the oxidation of tin, and was used as a face powder.

Compounds of lead and mercury—The ancient Taoists were much interested in these two metals, and pharmacologists therefore studied their compounds carefully.

The principal compounds of lead which were known to the ancient Chinese were white lead (basic lead carbonate), red lead, litharge, lead sulfate, lead acetate, and lead tannate. White lead and red lead will be discussed in detail in the chapter on colors. According to the Chinese Materia Medica 8.7 litharge (PbO) was prepared by the following method: Lead was added to silver ore and the material was melted together to form an alloy of silver and lead. This alloy was put on top of a mass of wood ashes in a pit and was heated again. The lead was gradually absorbed by the ashes and the silver was left on its surface. When cooled, the silver was taken out and litharge was obtained from the pit after a long time. This method resembles the modern process of cupellation.

Among the compounds of mercury, mercurous and mercuric chloride, mercuric sulfide, and mercuric oxide were known. Calomel (HgCl) was prepared (Materia Medica 9.4) by a dry method which is different from the present wet method of the double decomposition of mercurous nitrate and sodium chloride. As mentioned in *Pen ts'ao* this method consisted in grinding one tael of mercury, two taels of alum, and one tael of common salt into a fine powder. They were put together into an iron vessel and covered with an inverted small basin and the connection was sealed tightly with mud. After about three hours, it was opened. The powder which sublimed on the basin was as white as snow. The yield was eight mace.

Mercuric chloride (HgCl$_2$) was called "frost powder" (粉霜). In the Chinese Materia Medica 9.5, a method of preparation was recommended from a book of the T'ang Dynasty as follows: Ten taels each of sulfur and mercury were heated in separate vessels. After a long while, they were mixed when the sulfur was still in a molten state and the mercury was hot enough. As soon as their original form no longer remained, ten taels of yellow earth taken from the furnace and one tael of common salt were added and mixed by stirring. On the bottom of the vessel was a layer of salt, above which was the mixture of mercury and sulfur covered with another layer of salt. An inverted earthen basin was put above it and sealed with the mixture of salt and mud. They were then heated for two hours and the "frost powder" which sublimed on the basin might be taken out by brushing. This sublimed product might be refined seven times by the same method with the addition of earth and salt.

Both *tan-sha* and vermilion were mercuric sulfide; the former was produced from the natural ore cinnabar, either directly or by a simple process of refining and the latter was generally prepared by the direct combination of mercury and sulfur.

Because *tan-sha* was red in color and could be decomposed into mercury, the alchemists deceived the people by stating that it could prolong life, as already mentioned in detail in the preceding chapter. Vermilion is a most valuable kind of pigment and will be discussed later.

Compounds of sulfur: Alum and Vitriol—Both sulfide and sulfate were studied by the ancient Chinese. Among the sulfide ores, they were best acquainted with pyrites, orpiment, and realgar. The first one was used for making sulfur and vitriol and the last two were only distinguished by their names corresponding to *"yin"* and *"yang."* There were several kinds of sulfate known in ancient times, the sulfates of calcium, copper, aluminum, iron (ferrous and ferric), etc. Gypsum, i.e., calcium sulfate, occurred in nature. White alum, the double salt of aluminum sulfate and potassium sulfate, was monopolized by the government in the time of the Sung Dynasty. Copper sulfate was known as "blue vitriol" (礬), ferrous sulfate as "green vitriol," and ferric sulfate as "yellow vitriol," respectively. The ancient people were much surprised that copper could be produced when iron was put into a solution of blue vitriol as has been described above. After the Sung Dynasty, green vitriol and yellow vitriol were prepared from pyrites (FeS$_2$) at the place where sulfur was produced.

The method as described in *T'ien kung k'ai wu* 11.58 consisted in heating pyrites and coal in a furnace on the top of which was a hole and above it an inverted earthen basin. When a golden yellow flame was emitted, sulfur sublimed on the basin. After being heated for ten days, the calcined product was taken out to be extracted with water and filtered. Green vitriol crystallized out from this solution. Yellow vitriol was obtained by the oxidation of green vitriol.

Acids, bases, and alkaline salts—The early Chinese, like the early Europeans, were acquainted with only one kind of acid, namely vinegar, but they were aware that the vapor produced by heating yellow vitriol was corrosive in property and that the gas produced by heating ammonium chloride would dissolve in water to form a solution which had the property of dissolving silver.

Lime, soda, and potash were bases frequently used in ancient times. Lime was manufactured by heating limestone or the shell of oysters, clams, etc., and mortar was also early prepared by mixing lime and sand. Sodium carbonate occurs abundantly in deposits in the north of China. Potassium carbonate was extracted from wood ash.

Soda-niter and saltpeter occurred in deposits on the ground and were used for making fireworks at a very early date. Gypsum and bitter salt (MgCl$_2$) have long been used for preparing bean-curd, to coagulate the protein in bean-milk. Common salt represents an important industry in China, and will be discussed separately in the following chapter.

Chapter 4—SALT

SALT is an article of great importance in our diet, and its discovery and use date from a very early time. According to Chinese legend (*Wu yüan* 10.36) salt was discovered by Su Sha (夙沙), a minister of the Yellow Emperor. In the time of Yü, the founder of the Hsia Dynasty, different kinds of tribute were demanded from various localities and the officer of Ch'ing-chou (青州) was ordered to provide salt to supply imperial needs. Among the officials of the Chou Dynasty (1100–255 B.C.), a "Salt Minister" was in charge of making and offering the tribute salt. The taxation of salt began at the end of the Chou Dynasty.

PROCESSES OF MAKING SALT

The processes of making salt in ancient times, for the most part, resemble those used at the present day. According to the variety of salt, sea salt, lake salt, or well salt, methods of preparation differ slightly. Rock salt is found in nature in a very pure state and no refining is required.

The processes of making sea salt comprised the following three steps:

Construction of the yards, wells, ponds, etc.—In the salt-yard, ashes were dried and the sea water evaporated. Near the seashore, a piece of land was chosen for constructing the yard and a reservoir was built for storing the water. Each yard was about twenty-four paces wide and eighty paces long. After being ploughed, the ground was evened off by

55

hoeing with mattocks. It was then irrigated by drawing up water from the sea and allowing the earth thoroughly to absorb the salt water. Having become dry, it was hoed, again irrigated with sea water, and dried once more. By means of mattocks, the yard was cut up into three or four parts, and shallow channels were dug for introducing the sea water so as to supply irrigation day and night (Figure 27). Over the even ground of the yard, the dried ashes were spread and the sea water was scooped up from the channels and sprinkled over them.

Ash-drainers were constructed by making square pits more than two feet deep and six or seven feet wide at a higher position but not very far from the salt-yard. These drainers were built of mud together with moistened grass, making their bottom firm and even, and building their sides perpendicular like the walls of a house. Small bamboo pipes were connected from one side of the drainer to the brine well or pond.

The well or pond was constructed for storing the brine. The pond was rectangular in shape, eleven feet deep, seven or eight feet wide, and more than ten feet long. Wells were round and of two kinds: one was larger with a diameter of six and a half feet and the other was smaller being only $3^1/_4$ feet in diameter. Both of these were as deep as the pond and the smaller one was distinguished by its name *kang t'ou* (缸頭). They were built of mud mixed with grass, their bottoms and sides being made very strong and firm to avoid any leakage. Bamboo pipes were buried under them for the purpose of conveying the brine to them from the ash-drainer.

Evaporation of sea water—The concentration of sea water for salt was carried on to some extent in warm, dry districts by solar evaporation, the sea water being exposed on the ground of the salt-yard to the sun's rays. The sea water was first drawn up by means of buckets and allowed to flow into

Figure 27. Drawing up sea water and introducing it into the salt-
yard.

Figure 28. Sweeping the salted ash into heaps after the sea water has evaporated.

Figure 29. Working the drainers for the preparation of concentrated brine.

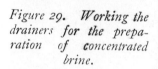

Figure 30. Final crystallization of the salt.

the channels from which it was again scooped up and poured on to the yard where it moistened the earth overnight.

On the early morning of the next day, the ashes were spread over the yard with wooden spades and swept evenly by means of bamboo brooms. After this, sea water was sprinkled with long-handled scoops so as to enable the ashes to adhere to the earth. After evaporation of the sea water for half a day, the ash gradually became impregnated with salt and then was swept together in many heaps all over the yard as shown in Figure 28. The complete drying required one day in summer and two or three days in winter.

All the dried and salted ashes were then collected into the drainers each of which was capable of holding about thirty piculs of ash. One picul of raw ash was put on the bottom of the drainer, then the salted ash, and then another picul of raw ash, and a bundle of straw was put on the top. Sea water was poured onto the contents of the drainer to dissolve the salt in the ash, varying in quantity according to the amount of salt in it. The brine formed flowing out from the bottom of the drainer was introduced into the well near it (Figure 29). It was further scooped up from the well and allowed to flow through a bamboo pipe into the brine boat, by which the brine was transported, and later was scooped up from the boat and allowed to flow through bamboo pipes to a small channel and finally to the pond for storage. The ash after draining was ready to be spread over the yard for use again.

Before the hydrometer was adopted, the concentration of the brine was determined approximately by putting a few pieces of *shih lien tzu* (石蓮子) (seed of *Caesalpinia minax*) of different size or weight into the brine to see which one floated on the surface. These seeds had been previously and individually tested in the same way in brines of various known concentrations, and therefore the floating of the pieces indicated the concentration of the brine which was tested by them.

Crystallization of salt—The salt was crystallized out by evaporating the brine in a pan over a fire. The pan was made of several pieces of iron plate fastened together and supported by a mixture of straw, ash, lime, and brine, standing on a stove.

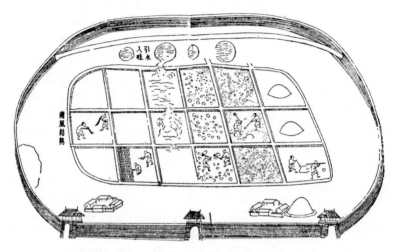

Figure 31.   Plant for producing lake salt.

The brine was drawn into the pan for boiling. In each pan, one or two square or round wooden frames, called "salt-bed" (鹽床), covered with strips of bamboo were used for holding the crystallized salt as shown in Figure 30. The bitter liquor was then drained off through the spaces between the bamboo strips, and damp salt was thus obtained. If the brine was dilute the "salt-bed" was not used, the small amount of salt obtained being taken out with iron spades. The stove ash was used for spreading over the salt-yard as before stated.

Lake-salt was mostly produced in Kansu and Shansi. Wells were generally built around the salt lake. A piece of land at the border of the lake was ploughed into plots separated by dikes (as shown in Figure 31) into which the clean water from the lake was introduced. This operation was always carried out in the spring. After the summer and the autumn, when the wind blew severely, salt in large crystals was deposited in one night. This was often used as table salt.

Well-salt was produced in large quantities in the southwest of China. Brine was obtained from bored wells. The mouth of the well was lined with stone circles, one above the other, their interstices being filled up with small pieces of stone, and each having a central hole about nine inches in diameter, as shown in Figure 32.

Figure 32. Preparing the top of a salt well before drilling.

The work of boring was very difficult and a great number of devices were made in order to overcome the numerous obstacles encountered. The tool used for drilling was a chisel-shaped piece of iron, seven or eight feet long and weighing more than one hundred catties, the cutting edge of which was about one foot broad by two and a half inches thick, resembling the tail of a fish and therefore called a "fish-tail chisel." This chisel was attached to a length of bamboo which, in turn, was fastened to an iron ring, tied to a rope which passed over a pulley at the top as shown in Figure 33. During the drilling the whole apparatus was operated by men or oxen, making a downward stroke to the earth, capable of boring more than one foot every day and night. When the operation had been carried on to a depth of more than three hundred feet, the drilled well was lined with wood in order to exclude the water from the overlying strata. This wooden lining was made of upright and round fir timbers, each about ten feet long, cut vertically into two halves and having the central portion removed. Each length was attached to the next with proper connections and was wrapped round with cloth, flax, tung oil, lime, etc., to make it water-tight and suitable for the purpose. More than twenty of these lengths of fir were required for each well. After the wooden lining had been set in place, a small tool was used for boring. The cutting edge was like a silver-ingot, and so derived its name "silver-ingot chisel." During this stage of drilling, a very long time, several years or even more than ten years, was required and many difficulties encountered.

At frequent intervals it was necessary to remove the mud and splinters of rock. This was done by the "sand-pump" which was a long bamboo pipe, bound up strongly with flax thread, having a valve at its bottom. It was tied to the bamboo in place of the "fish-tail chisel" and lowered to the bottom of the well. The water, which was always present or introduced into the well if required, rushed into the pipe, drawing the débris with it; then the valve was closed and the tool was at once raised. Boring was continued after each of these operations.

When the earth was bored to the depth of more than 1200 feet, the "yellow" brine was found and below 2500 feet, the "black" brine, the latter containing more salt. The tool used for raising the brine was like the "sand-pump" just

Figure 33. Drilling a salt well.

Figure 34. Making the pipe for the well.

Figure 35.   Sinking the pipe.

Figure 36.   Pumping brine.

described.   Figures 34 and 35 show the making and sinking
of the pipe.   The well was operated by oxen as shown in
Figure 36.   Eight or nine pipes full of brine could be sucked
up into the pan every two hours.   At the bottom of the pan
was a hole, from which the brine ran through the bamboo
pipe underneath the earth into the storing room.

In the province of Szechuan the brine from the well was
drawn from the storing room by passing through a very long
bamboo pipe to the evaporating room where it was evaporated over a fire of natural gas.   At the mouth of the gas-well
a wooden well-head was built, about ten feet wide and ten
feet deep, from the side of which a bamboo pipe led away
as far as ten *li* (里) (about 3 and $1/3$ miles) to the evaporating
room.   The gas escaped into the upper part of the stove from
a hole as big as one's finger above which the salt pan was
placed.   When lit the gas flame was bright and two or three
inches long.   The brine was evaporated to the right degree
of concentration as in the crystallization of sea-salt, which
this product resembles closely.

Chapter 5—CERAMIC INDUSTRIES

Porcelain, *tz'u* (瓷), is fine and decorated pottery. Pottery known as *t'ao* (陶) in China is the coarsest porcelain. Both are earthenware. Owing to the improvement of its manufacture the term *tz'u* was gradually used instead of *t'ao*.

The manufacture of pottery commenced very early in human history and Chinese legend attributes it to the ruler Shen-nung (神農). The same legend also has it that the first Superintendent of Pottery (陶正), Ning-fong (寧封), was appointed by the Yellow Emperor, thus beginning the so-called *"Kuan yao"* (官窯) (imperial factory) of the subsequent dynasties. Further, in the time of the Emperor Yao (堯) (one of the Five) and his successor, the Emperor Shun (舜) (one of the Five), earthenware was more extensively used, not only for domestic but also for sacrificial purposes and many names such as earthenware *ta* (瓦大), *t'ai-tsun* (泰尊)—for sacrificial use—earthen-*liu* (土瑠), earthen-*hsing* (土鉶), earthen-*kuei* (土簋), *tseng-p'en* (甑盆)—for domestic purposes—were attributed to that time. Emperor Shun is even said to have fashioned pottery himself at Ho-pin (河濱) and made household wares at Shou-ch'iu (壽丘).

The ceramic industry developed also in consequence of the advance of architecture. It is said that brick and tile were also first made by Wu Ts'ao (烏曹) and K'un Wu (昆吾) in the time of the Emperor Yü, the founder of the Hsia Dynasty. A great many earthenware objects were produced

66

Figure 37. Porcelain pitcher of the T'ang Dynasty, decorated in three colors.

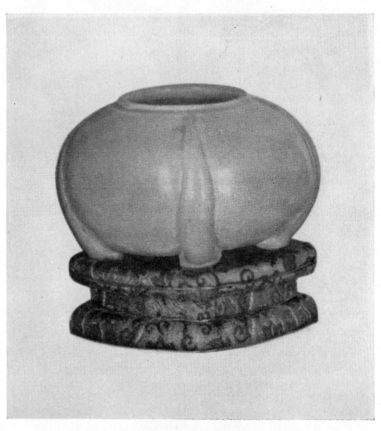

Figure 38. Yüeh Yao of the T'ang Dynasty.

in the Shang Dynasty, and some of them have been recently recovered by excavation.

The wares of the Chou Dynasty were produced in various shapes: *kuei* (簋), *tou* (豆), *li* (鬲), *yü* (庾), *t'ai* (甂), etc.

A book which describes an idealized organization of the Chou government mentions a man in charge of pottery who had the title *Chuan Chih* (塼埴). It is stated in *K'ao kung chi* 41 that for the fabrication of pottery there are two classes of workmen: those who fashion it on the wheel are called *T'ao Jen* (陶人) and those who mold the clay, *Fang Jen* (瓬人), and that the former makes the cauldrons, *yen* (甗), the basins, *p'en* (盆), the colanders, *tseng* (甑) and other vessels, *li* (鬲) and *yü* (庾) and the latter makes the sacrificial vessels, *kuei* (簋) and *tou* (豆). Thus we know that *T'ao Jen* and *Fang Jen* were in charge of making the vessels for domestic use and for sacrificial purposes, respectively, in those times.

During the Han Dynasty (206 B.C.–A.D. 220) the development of the ceramic industry attained to such a degree of excellence that *t'ao* (pottery) was improved into *tz'u* (porcelain) and so this period may certainly be regarded as the time of the birth of porcelain. The Chinese character "*tz'u*" first appeared in an ode written by Tsou Yang (鄒陽) of the time of the Emperor Wu (140–88 B.C.) as follows (Han shu 19.7): "When the fermented mash has been finished, the green porcelain, *lu tz'u*, wares are then resorted to."

This great advance in the Han Dynasty was accounted for by the importation of "*liu-li*" (琉璃), glassy substance, and the invention of the potter's wheel, known as *chün* (鈞). At that time, China was in communication with Rome and other countries of Eastern Europe whence *liu-li* was introduced into China and the method of making it was copied to prepare a glaze for porcelain. The porcelain wares, however, made in that time were comparatively brittle and not very

durable on account of the low firing to which they were subjected. Ching-te chen (景德鎮), the center of the porcelain
industry in China, is said to have had no porcelain kilns
until the Han Dynasty. Many articles of the Han Dynasty,
such as bowls, plates, lamp sticks, jars, tripods, etc., have
been recovered from the tombs of that time.

P'iao tz'u (縹), appearing in a stanza of the ode of P'an
Yüeh (潘岳) (d. A.D. 309), was the renowned green porcelain
of the Chin Dynasty (A.D. 265–420). For this reason, this
dynasty has been regarded incorrectly as the period of the
beginning of porcelain making. At that time wares produced
from the yao (窯), of Ou (甌) or Yüeh (越) (now Wen-chou fu
in Chekiang province) were well known. For instance, Tu
Yü (杜毓) in his "Verses upon Tea" (荈賦) says: "Select
cups of fine porcelain from the yao of the Eastern Ou" and
Lu Yü (陸羽) in his Ch'a ching (茶經), "Description of
Tea," says: "The bowl produced from Ou or Yüeh is of
blue color, having the edge of the upper rim straight and
not reverted, the foot expanded below. It is shallow and
holds half a liter." Apparently the porcelain in question
was of blue color and identical with the so-called p'iao tz'u
appearing in the ode of P'an Yueh.

When the Chin Dynasty had been overthrown, the people
were governed either by the Northern or the Southern sov-
ereigns. The Southern Ch'en Dynasty ordered the factories
in Ch'ang-nan chen (昌南鎮), now Ching-te chen, to make
pillar bases of porcelain and send them to the capital, Chien-
k'ang (建康), as tribute during the first year of the era
Chihte (至德) (A.D. 583); while the Northern Wei Dynasty
(A.D. 386–534) established factories in Kuan-chung (關中)
and Lo-chung (洛中), respectively. Both the Southern and
Northern dynasties appointed officials to administer the
manufacture of porcelain.

It was during the time of the Sui (隋) Dynasty (A.D.
589–618) that an important contribution to the porcelain

industry was made by Ho Ch'ou (何稠). It is stated in his biography in the Annals of the Sui Dynasty (68.10) that he had a wide knowledge of ancient pictures and was a great connoisseur of antiquities. In his time, the art of making "*liu-li*" had long been lost in China but he made green porcelain to be used instead of it. To his invention the ancient Chinese owed this further achievement in the porcelain industry.

In the time of the T'ang Dynasty (A.D. 618–907) real porcelain produced by high firing was first made. In the period Wu-te (武德) (A.D. 618–626), T'ao Yü (陶玉), a native of Ch'ang-nan chen—now Ching-te chen—brought his porcelain wares, called wares of imitation jade, to the capital and presented them to the Emperor.

Before the T'ang Dynasty, celadons or pale sea-green colors were favored. The colors of T'ang porcelain were blue, black, white, brown and of three-color decoration, being more beautiful than the monochromes of earlier times. In the fourth year of Wu-te (A.D. 621), a bureau was organized at Ching-te chen, the director of which was in charge of making porcelain for imperial use. Besides the porcelain made by T'ao Yü, and known as *T'ao-yao* in that time, the other famous *yao* of T'ang were as follows:

Ho *Yao* (霍窯)—This porcelain was of neutral tint. It was thin and made of fine materials. The best kind had a luster like jade. It was made by Ho Chung-ch'u (霍仲初), a native of Tung-shan li (東山里), and called Ho-ware in that time.

Shou *Yao* (壽)—The factories were founded at Shou-chou (壽州) in Chiang-nan (江南). The color of the porcelain was yellow. *Ch'a ching* (茶經) states that Shou-*tz'u* is bad, as its yellow color does not match the purple color of tea.

Hung-chou *Yao* (洪州)—Hung-chou is now Nan-ch'ang (南昌), the capital of Kiangsi Province. This porcelain was of a yellowish brown color, but it is stated in the *Ch'a ching* that the brown colored porcelain of Hung-chou would blacken the color of tea, its quality being inferior to the Shou-chou porcelain.

Yüeh *Yao* (越)—It was made at Yüeh-chou (越州), the original name in the times of Sui and T'ang, now Shao-hsing (紹興), in the province of Chekiang (浙江). The porcelain was of blue color, highly valued at that time. *Ch'a ching* says that for bowls, the Yüeh-chou porcelain is the best; it resembles jade and ice; it is blue and gives a greenish tint to the tea, in which the Hsing (邢) porcelain is inferior to Yüeh *yao*. The verses of Lu Kuei-meng (陸龜蒙) contain the following stanzas (*Ch'üan T'ang shih* 13.1):

> The misty scenery of late autumn appears when the Yüeh kilns are thrown open.
> The thousand peaks have been despoiled of their bright color for the decoration of the bowls.

Meng Chiao (孟郊) in one of his verses (*Meng Tung-yeh shih chi* 9.143) says, "Yüeh-chou cups are like molded lotus leaves." Ku K'uang (顧況) in his "Verse on Tea" says "The cups of Yüeh-chou paste resemble jade." From the above descriptions it can be seen that the Yüeh *yao* was a delicate porcelain of the time of the T'ang Dynasty.

Ting *Yao* (鼎)—This was made at Ting-chou (鼎), now Ching-yang Hsien (涇陽) in Si-an Fu. Lu Yü in his *Ch'a ching* classifies the porcelain bowl of Ting-chou as inferior to that of Yüeh-chou, but better than those of Shou-chou and Hung-chou.

Wu *Yao* (婺)—This was made at Wu-chou (婺), now Chin-hua (金華). *Ch'a ching* says that Wu *yao* porcelain is inferior to Ting *tz'u* but better than Shou-chou and Hung-chou.

Yo *Yao* (岳)—This porcelain was formerly made at Yo-chou in the province of Hunan (湖南). It was of blue color; it is spoken of by *Ch'a ching* as inferior to Wu *tz'u*. However, the blue color was suitable for the whitish red tinted tea, and so it was still better than Shao-chou and Hung-chou.

Shu *Yao* (蜀)—This was made at Ta-i (大邑) of Ang-chou (卬) in the province of Ssuchuan. The body was thin, fine and strong, being white colored with a nice resonance, and highly esteemed at that time. In the collected writings of Tu Shao-ling (杜少陵) (A.D. 712–770) there is included a verse of his (4.38), in which he begs from his friend a bowl of Ta-i porcelain: "Of porcelain baked at Ta-i so light and yet so strong; resounding like pure jade when struck, and famed through the city. Your Excellency has white bowls surpassing hoar frost and snow. Pray be gracious to me and send some to my poor mat-shed." From what has been described in the above stanzas as "light and strong as pure jade," and "surpassing hoar frost and snow," it appears to have been superior to any other kind of porcelain, even that which was produced in later years.

Ch'in *Yao* (秦)—This was made at the place which is now known as Ch'in-chou in the province of Kansu. It has been said that all the wares were bowls, cups, and the like, most of which were of one color without decoration, occasionally having the markings of fish-roe.

Hsing *Yao* (邢)—This was formerly made from the time of T'ang at the place which is now called Hsing-t'ai Hsien (邢台) of Shun-te Fu (順德) in the province of Hopei. The paste was fine and its color was plain. Formerly, it was known as white porcelain, but miscellaneous types with blue decoration are now made as well. *Ch'a ching* says that the Hsing-chou porcelain is generally considered to be better than Yüeh-chou ware. It is as white as silver or snow, while the color of tea is red, and for this reason, it seems to be inferior to Yüeh-chou. Although such criticism is based on consideration of its fitness for use in drinking tea, yet Hsing-chou porcelain is really delicate.

During the Five Dynasties (A.D. 907–960), *pi-se yao*

(祕色) of Wu Yüeh (吳越) and Ch'ai yao (柴) of Posterior
Chou (後周) were most famous. As stated in *T'ao lu*
(陶錄), *pi-se yao* was baked at Wu Yüeh. During the rule
of the House of Ch'ien (A.D. 907–976), the sovereign ordered
it to be baked for his special use, the officers and people not
being permitted to use it—hence its name "*pi se*" (prohibited
colors). However, it has been also said that it was a kind
or porcelain which had already been produced in the time of
the T'ang Dynasty.

According to *T'ao lu*, Ch'ai yao was baked at Cheng-
chou (鄭) in the province of Honan. It derived its name
of Ch'ai yao from Emperor Shih-tsung (A.D. 954–959) of the
Ch'ai family. It was as blue as the sky, as clear as a mirror,
as thin as paper, as resonant as a musical stone or jade, of
rich luster and delicate beauty, with a finely crackled glaze.
Its manufacture was perfect and color wonderful, it stood at
the head of the varieties of porcelain, but it often had coarse
yellow clay on the rim of the foot. Tradition says that when
a memorial was presented to the Emperor to ask about the
decoration required, the Emperor Shih-tsung wrote upon it:
"The blue of the sky after rain when the clouds have broken
is exactly the color which you should give to the porcelain."
At the present day, this porcelain ware is no longer to be
found. If a fragment or a broken piece were obtained and
mounted for a girdle-buckle or toy it would be highly valued.

During the Sung Dynasty (A.D. 960–1279) porcelain
ware of delicate appearance and good quality was produced,
and new designs in shape, color, and decoration were employed. These surpassed the achievements of former dynasties, and therefore this time has been regarded as a golden
period in the history of pottery and porcelain in China. This
success resulted in part from the development of the arts of
calligraphy and painting and the establishment of many
Imperial factories. Chinese porcelain ware was exported
from that time and came to be known as "china." It was

during these times that many factories, both imperial and private, became famous. The best reputed wares are now outlined as follows:

Ting *Yao* (定)—This was made at Ting-chou in the province of Hopei. The texture of the paste was fine. It was made in several styles, some covered with smooth glaze, others ornamented with designs executed in relief, painted decorations, or molded patterns. The most common designs were derived from the peony, lily, and flying phoenix. The best is white in color and of rich luster, of white paste covered with glaze. When the glaze had drops upon it like tears it was valued highly and was called popularly "powder Ting" (粉定) or "white Ting." Those of coarse make and yellowish color were of less value, and commonly known as "earthen-Ting." Su Tung-p'o (蘇東坡) (A.D. 1036–1101)—a very famous literatus of the Sung Dynasty—in his verse on "Boiling Tea in the Examination Hall" (11.11) says that the decorated Ting porcelain is like carved red jade. Only the two varieties of white and red color were admired at that time and the others as "purple Ting," "brown Ting," and "black Ting," were not esteemed.

According to the period of production, Ting-chou porcelain has also been classified as the "northern Ting" and the "southern Ting." The latter was made after the government had been removed to the South (A.D. 1127) and is of less value than the former.

Ju *Yao* (汝)—Among the different kinds of Sung porcelain, this may be ranked highest; compared with *kuan* (imperial) porcelain (官) of the period, it excels in form, structure, and luster. The paste had a rich luster like copper, and the body was either thick or thin, the thinner the better, the color being like "the blue sky after rain," with a thick transparent glaze, resembling a deep layer of lard. There are two varieties: one has a copper-like body without markings, and the other, a copper-like body with the markings of fish-roe. The former is better. Those with the glaze exhibiting throughout a palm-leaf veining, with some resemblance to a crab's claws, are the best, and those glazed with powdered carnelian, and of pale blue color are also highly valued.

Kuan Yao (Imperial Porcelain)—In the periods Ta-kuan (大觀) (A.D. 1107–1110) and Cheng-ho (政和) (A.D. 1111–1118) of the Sung Dynasty, a manufactory of porcelain was established at the capital, Pienking (汴京), now K'ai-feng Fu in the province of Honan, from which the porcelain ware produced was called *kuan* (imperial) ware. It was of fine transparent paste and thin body. The color was blue with a slight pinkish tinge of two shades, deep or pale. The vessels had crab's claw marking, a brown mouth and iron-colored foot. In the period of Ta-kuan the bluish white, pale blue and deep green colored glazes were favored, but only deep and pale blue colors were glazed after the time of Cheng-ho. When the government of the Sung Dynasty had removed to the South (A.D. 1127), the director, Shao Ch'eng-chang (邵成章), erected a factory at Hsiu-nei ssu (修內司), in which he made porcelain after the former method and produced a kind of ware called *nei yao* (內) (palace porcelain) as well as *kuan yao*. The forms of the pieces were perfectly molded and decorated with a clear transparent glaze and they were generally admired in those times. Later, beneath the Altar of Heaven in the then southern capital a new kiln was built from which the wares produced were of poorer quality than those made before but they were also called *kuan yao* and had the same form.

Ko Yao (哥)—At the south of Lung-ch'üan Hsien (龍泉), there is the Liu-hua Mountain (琉華), and below is the village of Liu-t'ien (琉田). Natives of that place lived by making pottery. Two brothers belonging to the family of Chang (章), the elder and the younger, men of Ch'u-chou (處), were directors of two different factories at Liu-t'ien, and the porcelain made by the elder brother, named Chang

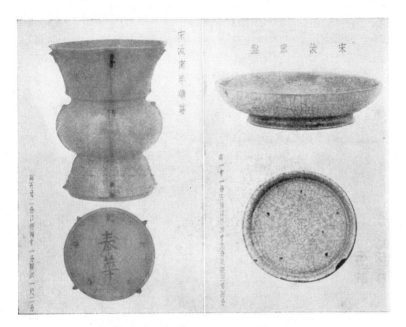

Figure 39. Ju Yao of the Sung Dynasty.

Figure 40. Kuan Yao of the Sung Dynasty.

Figure 41. Ko Yao of the Sung Dynasty.

Sheng-ii (章生一), was called, to distinguish it, *ko* (the elder brother's) porcelain. The paste was fine and thin, blue in color, of two shades, deep and pale. Some articles had an iron-colored foot and purple mouth. This *ko* porcelain has a number of broken lines upon it. It has throughout faint marks like fish-roe. The glaze used was of two colors, light yellow and pale blue.

Chang Lung-ch'üan *Yao*—This comprises the porcelain made by Chang Sheng-erh (章生二), the younger brother of Chang Sheng-i (章生一). The old name, Lung-ch'üan *yao*, was still kept for his porcelain. The thin body was made of fine paste. The color was bright, deep, or pale blue of different shades, being deeper than *ko yao*. Some articles had also the iron-colored foot without crackles. Compared with the old ware produced in Lung-ch'üan, it is finer and more excellent.

Chün *Yao* (均)—This was made in Chün-t'ai (均臺), namely Chün-chou, now Yü-chou (禹) in the province of Honan. It includes pieces of fine paste with glazes of nearly every color. Some pieces have the rabbit's hair marking. In classifying this porcelain, the rouge-like or vermilion red is placed first, next the bright blue, like onion-sprouts, and then the ink-like purple. Those of uniformly pure color with no stains are the best. This porcelain was scarcely recorded by scholars of the Sung and Ming dynasties. It is only stated in the *Hsüan-te ting i p'u* (宣德鼎彝譜) by Lü Chen (呂震) of the Ming Dynasty: "The Emperor Hsüan-tsung (A.D. 1426–1435) considered that the tripods in the altars and temples were not equal to those produced in earlier days, and then brought out the wares of Ch'ai, Ju, *kuan*, *ko*, Chün, and Ting of the Sung Dynasty stored in the Palace to be models for imitation." In this short writing, the Chün *yao* was mentioned along with *kuan*, *ko*, Ju, and Ting and thereafter it was generally esteemed.

Ching-te *Yao* (景德)—This was baked in the period

Ching-te (A.D. 1004–1007) of the Sung Dynasty. The thin
body was made of white clay. Its color is lustrous. The
Emperor Chen-tsung (A.D. 998–1022) ordered to be written
on the bottom of the tributary pieces these words: "made
in the period Ching-te." Since it was particularly beautiful
and delicate, the porcelain of Ching-te chen has been well
known and distributed throughout the whole of China.

All the porcelain wares mentioned above have been
famous, especially the *ko yao* and Lung-ch'üan *yao*, standing
in the first rank of the private manufactories and competing
with the *kuan yao*. When Ching-te *yao* had been established, many factories made a great variety of delicate wares
after the ancient models. On account of this fact, the town
of Ching-te chen was the ceramic center of the world nearly
one thousand years ago.

For the administration of porcelain making in the Sung
Dynasty, a Superintendent of Porcelain was also appointed
but with a different title from that of the T'ang Dynasty.
In the period Ching-te an officer was ordered by the govern-
ment to make porcelain in order to supply the imperial need.
This was the first porcelain officer to reside at Ching-te chen.

It is considered that the Sung Dynasty was, indeed, the
most prosperous period of porcelain making because of the
greater number of famed manufactories, the excellence of
the wares, and the delicacy of the styles, all being superior
to those produced in the former dynasties.

Little attention was given to the arts by the government
of the Yüan Dynasty (A.D. 1279–1368) when China was a
great Mongol empire but the porcelain officer was still
ordered either to make wares in obedience to a special imperial edict or to tax them. It is clear that with regard to
porcelain in the Yüan Dynasty the government was concerned with collecting the tax on it rather than controlling
its manufacture for imperial use. A greater number of
private factories were therefore set up during that time.

Shu-fu yao (樞府) and Hu-t'ien *yao* (湖田) were the two imperial factories of comparatively high renown. The wares produced by the former have a rich luster and a thin body made of fine and white paste. The types were mostly small footed with molded decoration, but sometimes of fine colors painted with gold. The pieces with a large foot were plain. There were various styles of pieces, such as tall footed bowls, dishes with curved rims, horse-footed plates, angular cups, etc. The inscription *"Shu-fu"* (Imperial Palace) was generally written inside them. Imitations were also made by the private manufactories, but only one per cent of them was selected for tribute, as they could never compete with *shu-fu yao*.

Hu-t'ien *yao* was situated at Hu-t'ien at the southern bank of the river in Ching-te chen. Pottery making was carried on there from the beginning of the Yüan Dynasty. The paste was stiff and coarse, being mostly of a yellowish black color. The pieces were rather delicate and were distributed through the east and west of Chekiang in those times.

As to the private factory, a worker in gold named P'eng Chün-pao (彭均寶) made porcelain, in imitation of Ting-chou porcelain, at Ho-chou (霍). The best was like the Ting porcelain and it was known at that time as new Ting-chou porcelain (新定器).

It is said that the porcelain wares of the Ming Dynasty (A.D. 1368–1644) were equal to those of the Sung Dynasty, but it can also be said that they were superior to them on account of the excellence of the wares and the delicacy of the decoration. In the second year of Hung-wu (A.D. 1369), an imperial factory was established at Ching-te chen by the order of Emperor T'ai-tsu (A.D. 1368–1398) with twenty imperial porcelain kilns. The wares made in the time of Yung-lo (A.D. 1403–1424) are said to have been better than those of the previous reigns. The number of imperial kilns at Ching-te chen was increased to fifty-eight in the time of Hsüan-te (A.D. 1426–1435) and to more than three hundred in the time of Wan-li (A.D. 1573–1619). Unfortunately, all of these kilns were destroyed by the followers of Li Tzu-ch'eng (李自成) in his rebellion of A.D. 1636. A brief sketch of the famous *kuan yao* of the Ming Dynasty is given below:

Hung *Yao* (洪)—The wares of Hung-wu (A.D. 1368–1398) were of fine paste and thin body with blue or black color, the plain ones being better. To make this porcelain, after the paste had been shaped, it was dried for a whole year before it was finished on the polishing-wheel and made thin; and after it had been covered with glaze and dried, it was baked; and, lastly, whenever the glaze was wanting in any place after the piece was taken out of the kiln, it was again polished and covered with glaze and baked anew. This shows why the glaze is as transparent and thick as massed lard, so that it does not readily chip or crack. At the private factories porcelain could not be made to equal this. Among the colored porcelain wares, the pots or cups of blue or black color, and painted with gold are excellent.

Yung *Yao*—These were produced from the imperial factories in the time of Yung-lo. The paste was fine. The body was generally thick, but sometimes very thin. The so-called *"t'o-t'ai"* (脫胎) (egg shell), pure white wares, and decorated and engraved porcelain, began to be produced after this time. Chu Yen (朱琰) in his *T'ao shuo* (陶說) says that among the ancient porcelain wares, blue was the color most highly esteemed, up to the Ming Dynasty, when the art of decoration with the *pi-se* glaze was lost, and the porcelain was all made pure white, either painted in blue or enameled in many colors. That of the reign of Yung-lo deserves appreciation, and may be ranked below the porcelain of Hsüan-te and Ch'eng-hua, but above that of Chiaching and Lung-ch'ing.

Hsüan *Yao*—This was baked in the imperial factories in

Figure 42. Lung-ch'üan Yao of the Sung Dynasty.

Figure 43. P'eng Yao of the Yuan Dynasty.

Figure 44. Celadons of the Ming Dynasty.

the reign of Hsüan-te (A.D. 1426–1435). The paste was red
in color. Materials for making the body and the colors used,
the vermilion, etc., were of the highest grade. The blue
decorated porcelain was most valuable. The faint color was
favorable for the background of the porcelain, but the
deeper for painting. Generally, it was in pure white color
with palm-leave spots, and beautified with a bright red glaze.
All the ware is strong and firm and does not easily crack or
break. Nothing inferior was produced, the various kinds of
small art objects being most elegant. This was the time
when Ming porcelain attained its highest excellence.

Ch'eng *Yao*—This was baked in the imperial factories
of Ch'eng-hua (A.D. 1465–1487). The paste was fine and the
body was thin. The pieces of *"wu ts'ai"* (五彩), that is, with
decoration in vitrifiable and polychromatic enamels, are the
best. The ordinary material was used for blue colors which
are inferior to the wares of Hsüan-te, but the painted porcelain is superior to those made before or after, as stated by
Chu Yen in his *T'ao shuo* who says that the best Ch'eng-hua
porcelain is that painted in enamel colors.

Formerly, the porcelain of Ming had been classified as
Hsüan *yao*, the first, Ch'eng *yao*, Yung *yao*, and Chia *yao*
next in order, but the painted ware of Hsüan-te is, in fact,
inferior to Ch'eng *yao* because the latter was painted more
vividly than could be done by any ordinary artist.

Cheng *Yao* (正)—This was the ware produced from the
imperial factories of Cheng-te (A.D. 1506–1521). The paste
was fine, the body varying in thickness. The color was blue
or polychromatic, *chi-hung* (霽紅) (deep red), a mineral silicate of copper being used for the best color.

Chia *Yao* (嘉)—This was the ware, made in the imperial
factories, in the time of Chia-ching (A.D. 1522–1566), of fine
paste and fine body. In the decoration of this kind of porcelain, Mohammedan blue (回青) which was the best kind of
cobalt ore and formerly obtained from Arab traders, was

much used. The red mineral was not to be obtained, and the processes of manufacture were slightly inferior to those of the previous reigns. A red color derived from an iron mineral, was the only red that could be fired over and over again. Therefore, the blue decoration was preëminent, the polychromatic and enameled decoration being fairly good, but in style and manufacture the ware was not nearly as good as that of Hsüan-te and Ch'eng-hua.

Lung-Wan *Yao* (隆萬)—This was the ware produced in the times of the emperor Mu-tsung (A.D. 1567–1572) and Shen-tsung (A.D. 1573–1619). The paste was fine; the body, either thick or thin; the color, either blue or polychromatic. The craftsmen were more skillful and there was nothing they could not make. Those in which the glaze, transparent and thick as massed lard, rises in millet points like the skin of a chicken or the peel of an orange, are admirable.

Besides the *kuan yao* described above, some famous private factories were as follows:

Ts'ui Kung *Yao* (崔公)—Ts'ui Kung, who lived in the time of Chia-ching and Lung-ch'ing, had the technique of pottery making. He followed the methods of Hsüan *Yao* and Ch'eng *Yao*. For sale everywhere, his wares stood in the first class of those made by the private factories.

Chou *Yao*—Chou Tan-ch'üan (周丹泉) lived in the time of Lung-ch'ing and Wan-li; a native of Wu-men (吳門), he came to Ch'ang-nan (昌南) to make porcelain. He was an eminent craftsman of pottery at that time, with experience in imitating old wares. When any piece had been finished by his hand, people purchased it at the highest price. He was proud of his own products and used to carry them to Soochow, Sung-chou (松), Ch'ang-chou (常), and Chenkiang (鎮江) in order to make a good bargain. No one could distinguish his wares from the famous ones of an earlier date. It is said that he made imitations of Ting tripods, of Ting ware, of the tripods of Wen wang (文王), of the tripods with animal-figured face and lance-figured ears so like the genuine ones that they were sold for thousands of taels each.

Hu Kung *Yao* (壺公)—This porcelain was baked in the time of the Emperor Shen-tsung (A.D. 1573–1619). The craftsman, with the pseudonym of Hu-yin tao-jen (壺隱道人), made every kind of ware of the highest quality by using the best grade of materials and colors. The inscription was of these four words: "Hu-yin tao-jen." Tradition says that the real name of the potter was Hao Shih-chiu (昊十九), but where he lived is not known.

All the emperors of the Manchu Dynasty (Ch'ing Dynasty) (A.D. 1644–1912) had a high esteem for artistic and literary works, so that porcelain wares were also made equal to those of the former dynasties. The name of the factory at Ching-te chen was changed from "Imperial Wares Factory" to "Imperial Porcelain Factory" by the order of the Emperor Shun-chih (A.D. 1644–1661), and the Ming *yao* which had been destroyed by the rebellion was partially restored. In the time of K'ang-hsi (A.D. 1662–1722), they were completely rebuilt. In the seventeenth year of the reign of K'ang-hsi (A.D. 1678), an official of the imperial household was sent to reside at the Imperial Porcelain Factory to supervise the manufacture of porcelain for imperial use. He exerted great efforts to make and to imitate the old wares and to invent new designs. Tsang Ying-hsüan (臧應選) was appointed director of the Imperial Porcelain Factory (in A.D. 1682). He was in office for several decades and also did his best to manufacture a great number of famous wares, known as Tsang *yao*. Tradition says that during Tsang's administration, gods frequently appeared in the flame, coming to protect the wares at the time of baking. Afterwards, Lang T'ing-tso (郎廷佐), the Viceroy of Kiangsi, made porcelain in imitation of those of Ch'eng-hua and Hsüan-te, also famous for a time and known as Lang *yao*. During Yung-cheng (雍正) (A.D. 1723–1735), the imperial

factories at Ching-te chen were directed by Nien Hsi-yao
(年希堯) (appointed about A.D. 1723), who selected the best
materials to make porcelain of highest excellence, imitating
the ancient wares and inventing new forms skillfully and
elegantly. They were known as Nien *yao*. The Emperor
Kao-tsung, namely Ch'ien-lung (A.D. 1736–1796), liked
literature and the arts very much. Every official who super-
vised pottery making could make porcelain by imitating
antiquity, inventing new designs, and using both foreign
and Chinese methods. By exhibiting the results of his
efforts he could curry favor with the emperor. In those
times, the directors of the imperial manufactories were first
T'ang Ying (唐英) and later Liu Pan-juan (劉伴阮). Both
of them selected their various materials carefully to make
porcelain of refinement, brilliancy, and purity, and reproduce
the different kinds of ancient ware of famous *yao* with equal
excellence. By employing the most experienced craftsmen
to do their best, nothing that was made was not gorgeous.
Meanwhile, princes or officials of the highest rank used to
have a kind of porcelain ware with the inscription of the
names of their own residences. The wares inscribed with the
so-called "Ku-yüeh-hsüan" (古月軒), said to be the name
of one of the buildings in the Palace, have been most famous
and precious. During the period Chia-ch'ing (A.D. 1796–
1820) and Tao-kuang (A.D. 1821–1850), the porcelain industry was but little developed. Unfortunately, when the
T'ai-p'ing rebellion broke out in the year 1850, the factories
at Ching-te chen were almost destroyed and the porcelain
industry in China declined. However, there was a revival
during Kuang-hsü (A.D. 1875–1908), and therefore it is
stated in *Shuo tz'u* (說瓷) that, although the ceramic industry during Kuang-hsü had not yet recovered to a condition
as good as that of K'ang-hsi and Ch'ien-lung, it was not
much inferior. From Hsüan-t'ung (宣統) (A.D. 1909–1912),
the last emperor of the Ch'ing Dynasty, to the Republic,

Figure 45. Decorated porcelain ware of the Ming Dynasty.

Figure 46. Decorated porcelain ware of the Ch'ing Dynasty (Ch'ien-lung).

civil war and foreign aggression caused Chinese industry to decline in every field, that of porcelain not excepted.

THE MANUFACTURE OF PORCELAIN

The processes of making porcelain wares may be briefly described as follows:

Materials—Chinese porcelain is composed of two chief ingredients, China-clay (or *kaolin*) and China-stone. The former is an infusible substance, a white aluminum silicate, produced by the decomposition of granite or feldspar and the latter is another compound of aluminum and silicon and is fusible. These two kinds of material are mixed together to make the body of the porcelain. The China-stone serves to bring the whole into a state of flux at a very high temperature and gives porcelain its vitreous or glassy character. To make glaze, the China-stone is also used and softened with a little lime, the proportion being varied according to the nature of the article. The districts surrounding Ching-te chen are well supplied with these materials which are prepared by collecting the proper stones. Mines are excavated to dig out the stones, which, when broken, exhibit internally black markings like seaweed. The natives take advantage of the streams flowing down the mountain side to erect wheels provided with crushers. The stones are finely powdered, washed clean, and made up in the shape of clay-bricks called *pai-tun* (白木). All the different kinds of earth used in the making of porcelain are included in this name.

Washing and purification of the earth—In making porcelain, the material must first be purified. The method is to mix it with water in a large earthenware jar, and to stir the mixture with a wooden paddle, till all the impurities have floated to the surface. It is next passed through a fine horsehair sieve and then into a bag made of doubled silk. It is afterwards poured into several earthenware vessels, so that the water may be run off and the moistened earth allowed to settle. Wooden boxes with no bottom are used, and placed on piles composed of several tiers of new bricks, covered with a large cloth of fine cotton, upon which the moistened earth is put, wrapped round with the cloth, and pressed with more bricks so that all the water may be drained away. When freed from water the prepared earth is thrown onto large stone slabs, and turned over with iron spades till it is quite ductile and fit for the manufacture of porcelain.

Manufacture of the cases (saggers)—A fierce blast of air and flame into the kiln would injure the soft paste and stain or break it. For this reason, it is necessary to use saggers, which are made of a mixture of earth and sand and are baked in the kiln. They are fashioned on the wheel in the same way as the porcelain. The work need not be too finely finished, and they are partially dried to fit them to be roughly shaped with the knife. The empty cases are first heated in the kiln before the baking of the porcelain.

Preparing the molds—In the manufacture of the round wares, each requires a mold so that the form and size may be alike. The molds must be made after the pattern required, but the size cannot be exactly measured, because the paste contracts and solidifies during the firing process till it is only seven- or eight-tenths of its original dimension. A good practical knowledge both of the time of firing and of the nature of the paste is required, before it is possible to estimate the amount of decrease in size, so as to fix the proper form of the molds.

Treatment of colors—The colors used on Chinese porcelain are obtained from certain minerals or metallic oxides and salts, and are made to adhere by the aid of some vehicle, The usual colors are green, yellow, red, dark violet, blue, and turquoise. They are derived, respectively, from minerals of copper, antimony, iron, manganese, and cobalt. They should be pulverized, washed, packed into small earthen cases, and dried in the kiln before use.

The grinding of the colors is shown in the right foreground of Figure 47. The mortars are placed upon low
benches. To the benches are fixed upright wooden poles.
which support the horizontal pieces of wood pierced to hold
the handles of the pestles which are kept revolving either
by one or by both hands.

*Figure 47. Manufacture of porcelain. Molding the paste, drying
small pieces on racks, grinding the colors.*

Fashioning the ware—Porcelain is made in more than
one form. Square, polygonal, ribbed, and angular pieces are
worked into shape by joining, by chiseling, by molding and
by carving; while the round pieces have the paste turned
on the potter's wheel. Larger pieces are turned of more than
one foot in diameter, small ones measuring less than a foot
across. The wheel, which is like a round wooden table, is

fixed so as to turn upon a perpendicular axle and revolves continuously for a long time. The turner sits upon the border of the apparatus and turns the wheel with a bamboo staff. After the wheel has been set in motion, he molds the paste with his hands upon the wooden head of the axle extending out from the center of the table. The vases which are round are turned in the same way as round wares. The polygonal, square, ribbed, and angular pieces have the paste wrapped up in cotton and pressed with boards into slabs, which are cut with the knife into sections, and cemented together with some of the original paste mixed with water.

Molding the paste—After the paste has been fashioned on the wheel and fixed by being dried, it is put into the finishing mold and pressed down gently with the hand until regular in shape and uniform in thickness. As shown in Figure 47. It is then taken out and dried in the shade, and finally polished with the knife.

Turning the unbaked ware—The size of the round ware is fixed in the mold, but to be polished smoothly, it is given to the cutter. A wheel is also used for polishing, and likewise furnished with a wooden mandrel in the center, the size of which is proportional to that of the ware. This has a round head, called "top-bell" which is wrapped round with raw silk, to protect the interior of the piece from injury. When ready to be turned, the piece is put upon the mandrel, the wheel is put in motion, and it is pared round with the knife, till it is polished quite smooth inside and outside. Each piece, when first fashioned upon the wheel, has a paste handle left under the foot, two or three inches long, to hold it by, while it is being painted and glazed. When all this has been done, the handle is removed, the foot hollowed out, and the mark written underneath.

Painting the ware—The decoration on both round wares and vases is so intricate that one piece may have hundreds or even thousands of separate lines. The men who sketch the outlines learn how to design, not how to paint in colors, while those who fill in the colors are taught coloring not designing, by which means the hand becomes skillful in one art and the

Figure 48. Turning round pieces of the paste on the potter's wheel.

mind is not distracted. The rings around the borders of the pieces and the blue bands are entrusted to the worker who finished the parts on the polishing-wheel; the seals, marks, and written inscriptions are the handiwork of a skilled writer. In the reproduction of living things it is necessary first to copy nature; in the imitation of antiques seeing many objects increases the skill of the worker.

Glazing the ware—The round wares and molded vases painted in blue, as well as imitations of ancient pieces of

porcelain, are all covered with glaze before being put into
the furnace. The glaze imparts its characteristic trans-
parency to porcelain and deprives the paste of its porosity.
Some colors which will stand the greatest heat are painted
on the body before glazing. The glaze is then applied and
the whole (the body and glaze) are burned at a single firing.
This type of ware is called "under-glaze." The oxides which
are more susceptible to extreme heat are applied over the
glaze, that is, after the body and the glaze have already been
fired once. These are called "over-glaze."

The ancient method of applying the glaze was to cover
the vase, whether square, tall, lobed, or ribbed, with a goat's-
hair brush filled with liquid glaze, but it was rarely distributed evenly by this method. The large and small round
are, and the round vases which were turned in one piece,
were dipped into the large jar which held the glaze, but they
became either too thinly or too thickly covered, and, besides,
so many were broken that it was difficult to produce perfect
specimens. At the present day the small round pieces are
still dipped into a large jar filled with glaze, but the vases
and the larger round vessels are glazed by blowing. A bamboo tube is cut one and a half inches in diameter and ten
inches long, and the mouth is covered with fine gauze. This is
dipped into the glaze, and then blown through from the
other end. The number of times that this process has to be
repeated depends on the size of the piece, and on the kind of
glaze, varying from a maximum of seventeen or eighteen to
a minimum of three or four.

Charging and firing the kiln—The porcelain being ready
for baking, it is taken to the kilns (Figure 50) which are
usually situated at some distance from the workshop. Each
kiln is oval and resembles a large inverted water jar in shape.
It is more than ten feet in height and breadth, and twice as
much in length and depth. It is covered with a tiled roof
like a house, and the building is called the kilnshed. Behind

this is built the chimney, which rises to a height of twenty-two feet outside the kilnshed. The ware when finished is packed in the saggers, and put into the kiln. As the ware is still in a soft state, great care must be exercised in placing it in the sagger. It is not touched, therefore, with the hand but transferred by an ingenious contrivance of cords and sticks. The saggers are placed in lines, leaving a small inter-space for the passage of the flame. The floor under each sag-ger is covered with a layer of sand and kaolin refuse in order to prevent adhesion. The fire is distinguished by three

Figure 49.   Applying the glaze to porcelain ware.

different parts, the front, middle, and back, and the saggers are arranged in the kiln according to the nature of the glaze, hard or soft. After they have been charged, the fire is lighted and the entrance of the kiln bricked up leaving a square hole, through which billets of firewood are thrown in without intermission. After the baking begins, a low fire is kept up for twenty-four hours, which is then followed by one more powerful. The firing is usually conducted at a temperature of from 1350° to 1450° C. At the top of the kiln are four or five small holes covered with broken pots, one of which is opened when it is thought the baking is completed, and by means of pincers a case is opened to test the condition of the porcelain. When the baking is finished, the firing is stopped, and after the lapse of another twenty-four hours or more, the kiln is opened.

Opening the kiln—The finish of the porcelain ware depends on the firing of the kiln. The process from the time of putting in to that of taking out of the kiln usually requires three days. While the saggers are still of a dull red color it is impossible to enter. After the kiln has been opened for some time, the workmen with their hands protected by gloves made of more than ten folds of cotton soaked in cold water, and their heads, shoulders, and backs, wrapped round with damp cloths, go into the kiln to take out the contents. When the porcelain has all been removed, and while the kiln is still hot, the new charge of ware is arranged in its place, in order that the damp ware may be dried by the heat, and be less liable to be broken into pieces or cracked by the fire.

Decorating the ware—For painting the round ware and vases of white porcelain with designs in the five colors, or in imitation of Western colors, it is necessary to combine the different colors after they have been pulverized finely, and to test the properties of the colors and determine the time of firing which they require. A clever eye, attentive mind, and exact hand are required to attain excellence. The colors are mixed with three different kinds of medium, the first turpentine, the second liquid glue, and the third pure water. The turpentine is useful for free coloring, the glue adopted for thin washes, the water for retouching the colors in relief.

Baking after decorating—After the white porcelain has been painted, it must be baked again to make the colors penetrate into the glaze. For this purpose, two kinds of stove are used, one open and the other closed. The open stove is

Figure 50. Kilns for firing porcelain. Charging the kilns in the background; filling saggers in the foreground.

used for the smaller pieces; the door opens outwards. A charcoal fire having been lighted all round, the pieces of porcelain are placed upon an iron wheel, supported upon an iron fork, by which it is passed into the stove, the wheel being made to revolve by means of an iron hook, so as to insure a uniform temperature. The closed stove is used for the larger pieces. This stove is about three and a half feet high and three feet across. It is surrounded by a double wall,

and the charcoal fire is put inside, the walls being perforated
below for the passage of air.   The porcelain is put into the
interior of the stove.   The stoker holds in his hand a circular
shield to protect him from the heat of the fire.   The stove
is covered with a flat slab of yellow clay, hermetically sealed,
and opened again after twenty-four hours.

THE MANUFACTURE OF BRICK AND TILE

The ancient and modern methods of manufacturing
brick and tile, according to *T'ien kung k'ai wu* 7.1–4, consist
in the following processes:

Brick—The clay used may be of blue, white, red, or
yellow color.   It is first moistened with water and trampled
by several head of cattle until it has the appearance of
sticky mud.   Then it is filled into wooden frames and its
surface is pared evenly by means of an iron wire bow so as
to form "paste."   When the "paste" has been made, it is
put into the kiln.   If the charge amounts to 3000 catties, it
takes twenty-four hours for firing; if 6000 catties, the time
required should be doubled.   There are two kinds of kiln,
the wood-kiln and the charcoal-kiln.   The flame which
issues from the former is bluish black, and that from the
latter is white.   At the top of the wood-kiln are three holes
for the emission of the smoke.   These holes are hermetically
sealed with mud until the fire is fierce enough and no more
wood is needed.   Then the kiln is "tempered" by pouring
water over its top.   This method, known as *"chuan yu"*
(轉泑), consists in making a flat surface on the top of the
kiln with a ridge on each of the four sides, over which the
water is poured, 2000 liters being required for 1500 kilograms
of brick.   By this means the temperature may be properly
regulated.   If it is too low, the brick, known as low-tempera-
ture brick (嫩火磚), will not be smooth and durable and will
retain the original color of the clay.   On the contrary, if the
temperature is too high, cracking marks will appear on the

surface of the brick or it will shrink, break, or bend and not be suitable for use. In order to determine the temperature the flame may be observed by looking at it from the outside through the holes of the kiln.

The charcoal-kiln is twice as deep as the wood-kiln and open at the top. It is packed with charcoal-cakes, two feet in diameter, and pieces of paste in alternate layers and then they are fired by throwing in burning straw or wood.

The materials for *liu-li* brick, colored glazed brick (琉璃磚), are the same as those for *liu-li* tile.

Tile—Clay free from sand dug from a depth of more than two feet under the ground is the material used. A cylindrical mold with four vertical lines on its surface is used. The clay, after being mixed with water and trampled thoroughly, is heaped up into a long rectangular piece

Figure 51. Making paste for tiles.

which is then cut into slabs of the thickness of $^5/_{12}$ inch each, by means of an iron-wire bow. The slabs are taken off like strips of paper and fixed on to the surface of the mold. When dried, four pieces of paste are left on each mold (Figure 51). After the "pastes" have been finished and completely dried, they are baked in the kiln for one or two days and nights, according to the amount of the charge in the kiln. The process of "*chuan yu*" is like that used in making brick. Various kinds of tile were made in this way except those generally used in the Imperial Palace, known as *liu-li* tile, colored glazed tile, which are in the form of sheet or semi-circular pieces. The mold used for making *liu-li* tile is made of bamboo or wood. The "paste" after being made is baked in the kiln; 100 catties of tile requiring 5000 catties of wood for firing. After removal from the kiln, the pieces are covered with a concoction of *wu-ming-i* (無名異)—pyrolusite (MnO_2), palm hair (棕櫚毛), etc., for blue color, or with *tai-che-shih* (黛赭石), ochre color, rosin, *p'u-ts'ao* (蒲草) (*Acorus*), etc., for yellow color and baked again at a comparatively low temperature in another kiln. The *liu-li* tile of beautiful color is thus obtained.

CLOISONNÉ

Chinese cloisonné, under the name of *fa-lang* (珐瑯) or *Ching-t'ai-lan* (景泰藍), is famous throughout the world. Its ancient name *Ta-shih-yao* (大食) probably originated from Ta-shih (大食) which is the ancient Chinese name for Arabia. This suggests that the process of making cloisonné was originally introduced from Arabia. Although we cannot know when it was first made in China, this art was highly developed during Ching-t'ai (景泰) (A.D. 1450–1457) of the Ming Dynasty and so it derived its name *Ching-t'ai-lan*. Formerly, the best was made in the province of Yünnan but from Yung-cheng (A.D. 1723–1735) and Ch'ien-lung (A.D. 1736–1795) of the Ch'ing Dynasty up to date, Peking has been the center for this industry. A great number of specimens are exported annually to America and Europe.

Precious stones, such as ruby, sapphire, emerald, etc., were used as colors for making cloisonné in ancient times. However, the materials now used are silica, borax, red lead, or other pigments. They are fused together and powdered for use as colors.

The art of making the cloisonné article is to make first a steel mold on which are cut the designed characters or figures in bas-relief. From this mold, a copper foundation with characters or figures in relief is made. Then the pulverized fused masses, colors, obtained by firing the materials mentioned above, are applied over the surface of the copper foundation leaving the decorations prominent. The article is finished by baking in a furnace.

A complicated method is employed to make a more delicate and permanent article. No steel mold is employed but the foundation is shaped by hand. Figures are made by attaching small pieces of copper wire to the surface of the foundation with mucilage, then soldered, and the whole article is baked in a furnace in order to ensure that the fragments of copper wire will unite firmly with the foundation. The concave spaces are filled with various kinds of color prepared as already described so as to produce a colored surface level with the copper wire and so to produce the desired design. The decorated article is then baked again in the furnace over a coal fire for from fifteen minutes to half an hour. The time required for this baking should be determined by experience; otherwise the product will be inferior. After baking, the article is polished repeatedly by means of a grinding wheel and fine, hard charcoal in order to make its surface smooth and even. Modern cloisonné is electroplated in order that the inlaid copper wires may be given the appearance and brilliance of silver.

Chapter 6—LACQUER AND LACQUERING

LACQUER is one of the products peculiar to China. Its discovery coincides with that of porcelain making and its use is just as extensive. It was early used as a writing material, when writing was done with a strip of bamboo dipped in lacquer.

Lacquered ware, according to Chinese legend, was first made in the time of Shun and Yü. The latter is said to have had lacquered vessels for sacrificial use, black outside and red inside. It is stated in the Book of History that in the time of Yü, lacquer and silk were offered as tribute. During the Chou Dynasty, as we know from archeological evidence, lacquer was used for the decoration of carriages, harness, bows, and ceremonial utensils. Later, it was further used for the decoration of houses, weapons, musical instruments, etc. To lacquer the outside of the coffin before burial is a custom which dates from a very early time.

In addition to the excellent properties of hardness and brilliancy, beginning with the Han and T'ang dynasties lacquered wares were made extremely beautiful by decorating them with painting, and by carving and engraving them. The use of lacquer for drawing pictures was common under the Han, and at the same time it was also adopted for painting the toilet cases of Imperial Consorts and for the decoration of royal carriages, painted with the patterns of tiger, deer, and bear. Lacquered wares of the Han Dynasty, excavated from Lo-lang in Korea, were found to have decoration in gold and silver considered to be the models of the golden and silvery flat lacquer of later generations, their painting and carving also attaining to the highest degree of excellence. It has been suggested that the so-called *t'i hung* (剔紅), carved red lacquer, of the Sung Dynasty and the *ch'uang chin* (戧金), lacquer painted with gold, of the Yüan Dynasty originated in the time of Han.

The lacquer industry of the T'ang Dynasty (A.D. 618–907) was developed to such an extent that not only *t'i hung* began to be made but also golden and silvery flat lacquer, lacquer painting, etc. These were all appreciated for their beauty.

In the time of the Sung Dynasty (A.D. 960–1279), *t'i hung* also known as *tiao hung* (彫), carved red lacquer, was universally admired. Gold and silver were mostly used for the foundation over which a few dozen or more coats of red lacquer were heavily applied. Then they were carved with the designs of figures, such as pavilions, flowers, and herbs, by clever artisans and skillful engravers so as to make them as beautiful as pictures.

Besides this, there was painted lacquer of various colors. The lacquered wares incrusted with mother-of-pearl which were collected in the imperial palace of Sung were also superb. Some utensils were inlaid with copper wires. The Sung Dynasty was a period of preëminence for the lacquer industry, with its great variety of specimens and skill of workmanship, just as it was for porcelain.

During the Yüan Dynasty (A.D. 1279–1368), at the village Hsi-t'ang (西塘) of the town Yang-hui (楊匯) of Chia-hsing (嘉興), in the province of Chekiang, there were two craftsmen, the one Chang Ch'eng (張成) and the other Yang Mao (楊茂). Both of them won great reputations for their works in red lacquer, *t'i-hung*, carved for the most part deeply and in high relief. Another artist named P'eng Chün-pao

(彭君寶), who lived also at Chia-hsing, became celebrated for his painting in gold on lacquer (*ch'uang chin*), and his landscape and figure scenes, pavilions and temples, flowers and trees, animals and birds, were all alike cleverly designed and finely executed.

In the period Yung-lo (A.D. 1405–1424) of the Ming Dynasty, the imperial factory Kuo-yüan Ch'ang (果園廠), directed by Chang Te-kang (張德剛), the son of Chang Ch'eng, revived the production of *t'i hung*, which was made by applying thirty-six coats of lacquer to the foundation made of copper, tin, or wood and carved with fine and skillful designs, more refined and elegant than those of the dynasties of Sung and Yüan. Those made in the period Hsüan-te (A.D. 1426–1435) were also excellent. At the same time, the other kinds of lacquer-ware, *t'ien ts'ai* (塡彩), pierced lacquer, and *tsui ts'ai* (堆彩), piled lacquer, were also beautiful and renowned. The former, in which the patterns of flowers and birds had been pierced through and filled up with colored lacquer, was polished as evenly as a piece of painting, and the latter was made by Fang Hsin-ch'uan (方信川) in Hsin-an (新安). Lacquer-ware incrusted with mother-of-pearl was also made in this reign.

During those times China had traffic with the Japanese and the Japanese method was partially adopted so as to attain to the highest excellence. Yang Yün (楊郡), a lacquer-artist of repute, after learning the art in Japan, having experience in making lacquer-ware by the use of various colors, especially with Japanese lacquer, depicted landscapes and scenes from life vividly, in such a manner as to make them appear superior to paintings, so that both the form and decoration made them extremely pleasing and delightful and highly appreciated by the Japanese.

In the period Lung-ch'ing (A.D. 1567–1572), Huang Ch'eng (黃成), otherwise named Huang Ta-ch'eng (黃大成) was capable of making *t'i hung* competing with that produced

*Figure 52. Cloisonné vase (Ch'ien-
lung of the Ch'ing Dynasty).*

(See page 102)

剔紅雕漆六桥式盒

Figure 53. A box of carved lacquer.

by the Kuo-yüan Ch'ang (果園廠), the imperial factory, and superior to any other private manufactory. He was not only well experienced in making lacquer-ware but also was so learned that he wrote two volumes entitled *Hsiu ch'i lu* (髹漆錄) in the period T'ien-ch'i (A.D. 1621–1627) describing the art of lacquering, which is said to be the only work on lacquering written in Chinese. China, however, lost it for a long time and it was fortunately reprinted and published by Chu Ch'i-ch'ien (朱啓鈐) who obtained it from Ōmura Seigai (大村西涯) in Japan more than ten years ago.

In the Ch'ing Dynasty the making of carved lacquer was further developed and excellent specimens were produced from Peking, Soochow, and other places. The Ch'ien-lung emperor (A.D. 1736–1795) was a great admirer of it; and under his auspices, the imperial factory made a good many pieces of furniture of every kind for his palaces, ranging from great twelve-fold screens, thrones, and chairs of state to small objects for toilet and other uses. He also had a number of panels, in this material, made to commemorate his victories and other notable events, and often added poems written by himself or for him by way of decoration. His successor, the Chia-ch'ing emperor (A.D. 1796–1820) also had a great number of fine pieces of carved lacquer-ware in his palace which were much esteemed. After the periods Tao-kuang (A.D. 1821–1850) and Hsien-feng (A.D. 1851–1861), there were crises within the empire and this industry gradually fell on evil days. Golden lacquer, painted lacquer, and flat lacquer, produced from the provinces of Fukien and Kwangtung were the best. The modern style of Foochow lacquer, well known as "*t'o-t'ai*" (脫胎) was evolved by a craftsman, named Shen Shao-an (沈紹安) about three centuries ago and has been continued by his descendants to recent times. It is remarkable for its fine surface, said to be due, in part at all events, to the use of silk instead of paper or canvas as a basis for the priming and also to the care with which properly seasoned and otherwise suitable wood is selected. A good effect is produced, the lacquered ware being fine, pretty, and as light as paper. On account of this, the lacquer of Fukien is the best known in the world.

LACQUERING

Chinese lacquer is the sap of a tree, the *Rhus vernicifera* (*ch'i shu* 漆樹), which is indigenous to China and is cultivated throughout the Central and Southern provinces. The *Rhus vernicifera* seems not to have been native to Japan, but must have been introduced into that country from China or Korea at a very early date, certainly not later than the sixth century of our era.

The method of collecting raw lacquer in China is very simple. The tree is tapped in summer when about ten years old, horizontal incisions being made from the foot of the trunk upwards, and in groups, alternately from left to right. At this stage, the sap is a white or grayish viscous fluid which darkens and hardens rapidly on exposure to the air. It is collected in large air-tight vessels and before use it is strained through a hempen cloth to remove fragments of bark or other impurities. In order to get rid of excess water and to give it a uniform consistency, it is stirred at a mild temperature or in sunshine. Except for the addition, if required, of coloring matter, it is then ready for use without further treatment.

Descriptions of the art of making lacquered ware are rare in Chinese literature. A special work dealing with the art of lacquering entitled *Ch'i ching* (漆經), written by Chu Tsun-tu (朱遵度), was lost long ago. The only one left for our study is the *Hsiu ch'i lu* as previously mentioned. The following descriptions are quoted from the "Chinese Lacquer" by Edward F. Strange:

The basis of lacquer-ware is almost always wood; though porcelain, brass, and white metal alloys were also occasionally used.

The wood is generally a sort of pine, of soft and even grain, worked, in the smaller pieces, to an astonishing thinness and evenness of texture. Large objects have, of course, sufficient substance for strength; but never an excess. When a wooden fabric of the object has been finished, its surface is carefully smoothed; all knots, pin-heads or projections of any kind reduced, cracks or other irregularities made good and luted as well as the joints with a composition of rice paste and lacquer until all is as even as possible. A dressing of lacquer is then applied to fill up the pores of the wood and provide a base for the processes that follow. On this is applied a priming consisting of one or two coats of composition, made by mixing lacquer with finely ground burnt clay or similar materials, which, when hard, is ground to a fine surface with a whetstone. Some of the old writers have said that in this composition, the Chinese occasionally used pig's blood and powdered quicklime. In other cases of old Chinese flat lacquer a priming of oil only was used, which would account for the thinness and generally be inferior. A period of at least twelve hours would be needed for the composition to be ready to receive its next coat, a layer of hempen cloth, linen, paper or, especially in the case of Foochow lacquer, silk. This is again smoothed with a knife, to receive several more dressings of fine composition, each being given time to harden, and to be ground to an even surface before the next application. On this, successive applications of lacquer are made until the required thickness is obtained; it is clearly understood that each must be dried and ground finely before the next is laid on. The extent of the work involved in these preliminaries will be better realized when it is understood that each coat of lacquer as applied is only of about the thickness of a thin coat of paint, and that this is further reduced by the repeated grinding and polishing operations.

The decoration of flat or painted lacquer proceeds on similar lines. The design is painted on the prepared ground with lacquer colored as required, is allowed to harden, and is then again overlaid with a thin coat of clear lacquer. Gold dust may be incorporated at this stage. It was made in a far wider range of colors, including turquoise- and slate-blue, several greens, a red as of wine-lees and a rose-red, white, aubergine or plum-color and a brilliant yellow, as well as the vermilion, brown, etc. Brushes of horsehair, wild pig's hair, or rat's hair, were used by the artists who did the decorative portion of the work.

The hardening process which is essential to every stage in the preparation of lacquer-ware is expedited and perfected by the presence of moisture; and one may say with truth that the lacquer dries in a moist atmosphere. For this purpose, the Japanese used damp boxes or chambers, and Chinese employed a similar expedient. The Ming manuscript referred to, states that the Chinese use a "cave" in the ground and place the objects therein at night, so as to get benefit of the cool damp air. In this atmosphere the lacquer acquires a degree of hardness that enables it to be polished with a whetstone, bone-dust, etc., to be engraved with lines having the clean-cut precision of copper-engraving and to be carved like ivory or box-wood. It can, moreover, be given a polish which in brilliancy is not inferior to that of glazed porcelain or enamels.

With regard to the carved lacquer, it was built up in the manner already described; but the process was continued until a much greater thickness was obtained, even approaching, in extreme cases, to nearly half an inch. When two or more colors were to be incorporated in the design, the layer of each had to be placed in the order in which it would ultimately be required; and it was necessary that each layer should be of exactly uniform thickness. Not until the whole mass was completed and of perfectly homogeneous texture could the cutting begin; for this was done, inwards, from the surface. Very careful general instructions are given by the Ming writer. Knives of various patterns were used, and these were to be kept sharp and well controlled, so that no slips should take place. The carving should be V-shaped in section, with clean direct cuts, but carried out with restraint; care being taken not to cut away too much lacquer at a time, so as to make the work "lean." There must be no hesitation. An excess of color rendered the lacquer brittle.

A favorite and very attractive method of decorating lacquer-ware was by the use of inlay of shell. For this purpose mother-of-pearl was employed or for large work the nautilus pearl shell.

Chapter 7—GUNPOWDER

GUNPOWDER is a mechanical mixture, and is the oldest explosive and a very important one. It was perhaps invented by the Chinese. According to various investigations its discovery arose in the development of the manufacture of firecrackers. It has been customary in China for centuries, and still is, to shoot off firecrackers in every home on New Year's eve. This custom had a superstitious origin, it being thought that devils would be frightened by the noise and driven away. The original firecracker was a bundle of split bamboo sprinkled with common salt. On being set alight these bundles burned with some amount of explosive noise. Later on other chemicals were tried instead of salt and, if the results were successful, retained in the manufacture of these simple fireworks. In course of time, the increased volume of noise and probably accidents caused by the explosion indicated the value of some mixture like that employed in the making of fireworks, for military purposes.

The manufacture of fireworks was developed in the time of the Sui (A.D. 589–618) and the T'ang (A.D. 618–907) dynasties. Ma Chün (馬鈞) had first made a kind of firework under the name of "fire-cane" to which, under the Emperor Yang (A.D. 605–616), some kinds of chemicals were added and burned for the imperial pleasure.

For military purposes, the so-called "fire-ball" and "fire-arrow" came first into use in the first century of this era. The Record of the Three Kingdoms (三國志) says that

113

when the army of Chu-ko Liang (諸葛亮) (A.D. 181–234) attacked that of Ho Ch'ao (郝超) by besieging one of his cities with tall ladders and military carts, both implements were finally burnt by the "fire-arrows" shot by the soldiers of Ho Ch'ao. According to another book (*Sung shih* 197.2), T'ang Fu (唐福) offered his newly made "fireball" to the Emperor Chen-tsung of the Sung Dynasty in the third year of Hsien-p'ing (咸平) (A.D. 1001). Such kinds of fire weapon were made of rosin and other inflammable substances different from those used in making gunpowder. It was not until the Southern Sung Dynasty (A.D. 1127–1279) that real gunpowder was invented by mixing the three principal ingredients, niter, sulfur, and charcoal, as recorded in *Wu ching tsung yao* 12 (武經總要) written by Tseng Kung-liang (曾公亮) of the Sung Dynasty. During those times, Yü Yün-wen (虞允文) (A.D. 1110–1174) made a kind of fire weapon called "thunderclap" and Wei Sheng (魏勝) invented another kind which consisted of niter, sulfur, etc. Proof of these facts may be found in the following:

In the battle of Ts'ai-shih (采石) of 1161 (*Shih wu yüan hui* 21.9), a kind of fire weapon called "thunderclap" was used. It was made of paper rolls filled up with lime, sulfur, etc. When these rolls were ignited an explosion took place which burst the paper wrappings and the gases generated rendered both soldiers and horses unconscious so that the enemy was defeated. Moreover, Wei Sheng (*Sung shih* 368.15) made a military cart from which "fire stones" were thrown out to as far as two hundred paces and the gunpowder used was made of niter, sulfur, willow charcoal, etc.

Further (*Hsü Tzŭ chih t'ung chien* 166.8–9):

When the soldiers of Chin (金) guarded the city Pien (汴) (now Kaifeng in Honan), those who were stationed on the city wall sheltered themselves behind cow hides and wind-shields. The Mongols attacked then with one kind of fire weapon and their screens were burnt instantly. But the soldiers of Chin defended the city by the use of "thunderclap" which was an iron can filled up with chemicals. On firing it sounded as loud as thunder and

could be heard as far away as one hundred *li*. The result of its
explosion could be felt over an area of more than half a *mou* (畝)
(Chinese acre). Its shattering power was so great that even iron
armor might be broken by its attack. Near the city, camps were
built of cow hide by the Mongols, but the "thunderclap" was suspended from an iron rope to be dropped down from the city wall
to attack the camps. When the fire burst out, all soldiers and cow
hides were shattered. The soldiers of Chin also used another kind
of fire weapon made of chemicals capable of bursting out to more
than ten paces. The Mongols were much afraid of these two kinds
of fire weapon.

The History of Chin (金史) 116.13 says that in the period
A.D. 1224–1234 P'u-ch'a-kuan-nu (蒲察官奴) defeated the
enemy by using a kind of fire weapon which was a cartridge
made of sixteen layers of paper charged with a mixture of
willow charcoal, iron dust, porcelain powder, sulfur, arsenic,
niter, etc. It is also said that when A-li-hai-ya (阿里海牙)
invaded Fan ch'eng (樊城) (A.D. 1273) the Emperor Shih-tsu
of the Yüan Dynasty (*Yüan shih* 128.6–7) obtained a new
fire weapon offered by I-ssu-ma (亦思馬), a Mohammedan
(回人), and ordered it to be introduced to the military front
to attack Fan ch'eng. After capturing this city, the army
moved toward Hsiang-yang (襄陽) city, the tower of which
was attacked by the same weapon, sounding as loud as
thunder. Similar records can also be found elsewhere.

As the Mongols conquered so large a portion of Asia and
threatened Europe in the thirteenth century, the art of making gunpowder may have been introduced to the West as
far as the eastern armies reached. During the period
Hung-wu (A.D. 1368–1398) of the Ming Dynasty (*Ying huan
chih lüeh* 2.20, 22), when the military prestige of a prince,
named Sa-ma-erh-han (撒馬兒罕), the son-in-law of the
Mongol Emperor, threatened Hsi yü (Chinese Turkestan)
some Europeans came to join his army as soldiers and took
back both gunpowder and guns to their own countries.

However, it is mentioned in western history that in the battle of Niebla of 1251, the Moors began to adopt fire weapons for attack and defense. This was the time of the beginning of the Mongol Dynasty in China. It is also said that an Englishman, Roger Bacon, of the thirteenth century or a German monk, Berthold Schwartz, of the fourteenth century, discovered gunpowder. In reality, Bacon obtained this knowledge from Arabia and the Arabians may have learned it from China. The gunpowder made by Schwartz was first used at the battle of Crécy in 1346, again at Augsburg in 1353. All of these were later than the time of the Chinese invention in the twelfth century as stated in *Wu ching tsung yao* and other books. Thus, it can be concluded, that gunpowder may have originated in China and that the time of introducing the method of its preparation to the West may have been during the Mongol Dynasty (A.D. 1279–1368).

Although the invention of gunpowder in China was so early, it was not until the beginning of the Ming Dynasty that metallic guns and cannons began to be adopted. It is stated in the History of the Ming Dynasty 92.10 that when the Emperor Ch'eng-tsu (A.D. 1403–1424) had conquered Chiao-chi (now the North of Annam), whence he obtained some guns and cannon, a military troop was organized by the order of the emperor to practice the use and manufacture of them. It also says that two bureaus in charge of making military arms and weapons were organized in the Ming Dynasty, and many kinds of military weapons as well as gunpowder under various names were known.

According to *T'ien kung k'ai wu*, the explosion of gunpowder was interpreted by the ancient theory that the property of niter is *"yin,"* negative, and that of sulfur is *"yang,"* positive. When these opposites meet, a violent explosion takes place which not only frightens people but also destroys all people and things in the vicinity.

THE ANCIENT METHOD OF PREPARING GUNPOWDER

According to *T'ien kung k'ai wu* 15.31, the chief ingredients of gunpowder are niter, sulfur, and charcoal of grass or wood. The charcoal was prepared by burning willow, fir, root of birch tree, bamboo leaf, sunflower, root of bamboo, egg plant, etc. Other materials, such as arsenic, ammonium chloride, vermilion, realgar, orpiment, borax, porcelain powder, *ya-tsao* (牙皂 *Gleditschia japonica*), ground pepper, stone-yellow (a kind of color), calomel, *ts'ao-wu* (草烏 *Aconitum*) *pa-tou* (巴豆 *Croton tiglium*), *tung* oil, rosin, etc., were sometimes added.

Niter, being one of the essential materials for making gunpowder and a special product of the Orient, was called "Chinese snow" by the Arabs. It is clear that niter produced in China was well known to the West in early times.

Figure 54.   Preparation of sulfur by burning the crude ore with charcoal.

T'ien kung k'ai wu deals with this substance as follows:

In certain localities, when the moisture has evaporated from the earth, a white substance appears on the surface of the ground. It is swept together and dissolved in water for purification. It derives its name *"hsiao"* (消, dissolve) from being easily soluble. When this crude niter is swept up from the earth, it is put into a jar to be soaked in water for one night. After removing the floating impurities, the mixture is transferred to a large pan. More quantities of water are then added and it is boiled until the niter is completely dissolved. As soon as the solution is concentrated enough it is poured into another vessel and allowed to stand overnight to let the niter crystallize out. The crystals floating on the top are called *"mang-hsiao"* (芒硝 sodium sulfate), the longer crystals "horse-teeth niter" (馬牙), and the impure crystals underneath *"po-hsiao"* (朴). If purification is required, it is again dissolved in water and boiled with the addition of a few pieces of turnip. This is then poured into a basin and let stand overnight for recrystallization. The pure crystals obtained are as white as snow and are called "basin-niter" (盆). Both "teeth-niter" and "basin-niter" may be used for making gunpowder. Before use, niter should be roasted either on a piece of newly made tile or in an earthen pot, according to the amount to be used. When the moisture has been expelled, the dried niter is pulverized in a stone mortar and mixed with a proper amount of sulfur and charcoal.

As regards sulfur, *T'ien kung k'ai wu* 11.60 also says:

The mineral is stacked up with cakes of charcoal so as to make a heap. Around the heap, a furnace is built up with earth in such a manner that it encloses coal and mineral to a total weight of about one hundred catties. The top of the furnace is covered with the residual slag of mineral and at its middle part a hole is made as shown in Figure 54. When the temperature is high enough, the yellow flame and golden light burst out through this hole from the furnace. An inverted porcelain vessel, having a rolled rim like a fish-intestine, is used for covering this opening. The sulfur vapor is condensed into a liquid in this vessel, and flows out through a pipe into a basin where the sulfur solidifies.

A similar process may be carried out by burning a mixture of charcoal and green vitriol to obtain sulfur as already stated in the third chapter. One catty of sulfur can be produced from thirty or more catties of green vitriol.

For making gunpowder *Wu ching tsung yao* 12 recommends one catty and four taels of sulfur (20 parts), two and a half catties of niter (40 parts), and five taels (5 parts) of charcoal. Modern practice employs six parts of niter for approximately one each of sulfur and charcoal.

Chapter 8—COLORS AND DYES

CHINESE INK

CHINESE ink differs from Western ink in its properties and in the materials from which it is made. It exists usually as a solid piece, square or oblong in shape, and is prepared for use by grinding with water on a flat stone known in China under the name of *yen* (硯), palette or ink-stone. Recently, ink in liquid form has been prepared and to a certain extent used instead of the old solid variety.

The principal materials used for making Chinese ink are lampblack and glue. They resemble the ingredients universally employed in the manufacture of printing ink, but differ from those used in the West for making writing ink. The pen or writing brush and the paper used by the Chinese being of a special character render Western writing ink unsuitable for Chinese calligraphy and vice versa.

Since the chief constituent of Chinese ink is carbon in the form of lampblack which is not affected by the influence of sunlight and air, Chinese writing does not fade and old writings and pictures made about two thousand years ago are still in existence in the Chinese museums. The Western iron ink does not possess this excellent property of permanence.

It is not known when the making of Chinese ink began. A bamboo stick was dipped into lacquer for writing in antiquity, and a round piece of ink was first made by mixing lampblack obtained from black lacquer and from pine wood in the time of Wei (魏) (A.D. 220–265) and Chin (晉) (A.D. 265–420). Another tradition, however, has it that the discovery of Chinese ink was made by either Hsing I (邢夷) of the Chou Dynasty or T'ien Chen (田眞) of the Han Dynasty,

As paper was invented in the Han Dynasty, the use of ink may have become more popular at the same time. Officers in charge of making ink were appointed. Ink was offered to the Emperor as tribute, and was sometimes bestowed on officials or scholars by the favor of the Emperor.

In the period of the T'ang Dynasty (A.D. 618–907) there were many ink-makers and the art of manufacture greatly advanced. After the Sung Dynasty (A.D. 960–1279) lampblack from oil together with camphor and musk were, for the most part, used for making ink, which at this time attained to a high degree of excellence. Ink made of lampblack from oil was also commonly favored during the dynasties of Yüan and Ming.

Wei Tan (韋誕), otherwise named Wei Chung-chiang (仲將), living at the time of the Wei Dynasty (A.D. 220–265) was the first man to become famous as an ink-maker. *Mo ching* (墨經), "Description of Chinese Ink," describes his art in detail and Hsiao Tzu-liang (蕭子良) (d. A.D. 494) praised his ink by saying that just one drop of it was as black as lacquer. Tsu Min (祖敏), an officer for making ink in the T'ang Dynasty and a native of I-ting (易定), also possessed good technique in this art and was very famous in China during his lifetime. At the end of the T'ang Dynasty Li T'ing-kuei (李廷珪) and his son went to She hsien (歙縣) of Anhui from I-shui (易水) of Hopei and there produced a better ink than had been known before. Their method was thus introduced to the southern provinces. The *Mo ching* speaks of their ink as being hard as jade and as firm as rhinoceros horn, less than $1/6$ or $1/4$ inch of a stick of this ink was needed to cover several dozen pieces of paper with writing. Therefore, it was said that during the Hsüan-ho period

*Figure 55.   Imperial
brush or hair-pencil.*

Figure 56. Chinese writing materials; cakes of ink, ink-stone, and brushes.

(A.D. 1119–1125) of the Sung Dynasty, their ink was so valuable that gold was more easily obtainable than it. P'an Ku (潘谷), well known as an ink-maker in the Sung Dynasty, was highly praised by the very famous literatus Su Tung-p'o (蘇東坡) (A.D. 1036–1101) who wrote a poem in praise of him. Chang Ku (張谷), Yeh Mao-shih (葉茂實), Shen Kuei (沈珪), and others were also famous ink-makers in those times.

Since the dynasties of Yüan and Ming, Chinese ink has been generally made with lampblack from oil. In the K'anghsi period (A.D. 1662–1722) of the Ch'ing Dynasty, Ts'ao Su-kung (曹素功), an ink-maker in Hui chou (徽州) of Anhui province made the best ink, well known as *Tzu yü kuang* (紫玉光). After the T'ai-p'ing Rebellion (A.D. 1850–1864), Hu K'ai-wen (胡開文) succeeded him and his fame extends to the present.

THE PROCESSES OF MAKING CHINESE INK

Materials—The lampblack was made either by burning pine wood or vegetable oils. The process of making lampblack from pine wood was carried out by using a vertical kiln, more than ten feet high, having a wide belly and a small mouth. Instead of the chimney, at its top there was a jar of a capacity of fifty liters, on which five others were put one upon another. They were of different sizes, each having a hole at its bottom. The diameter of the holes varied according to the size of the jar. The spaces between these jars were closely sealed with mud. When the lampblack produced in the jars gradually became thick, the fire was stopped and the lampblack was swept out by means of a feather brush. Two, three, or five varieties of the product might be classified but that collected in the first vessel was not suitable for use.

The horizontal kiln has been used in later years. It is one hundred and twenty-five feet long, about six feet wide, and four feet high. The diameter of its mouth is about one foot. Generally, only three to five branches of the pine tree are burned slowly in it at one time. If more than this, the smoke rises up so heavily and quickly that the resulting product will be too coarse. This process may be accomplished in seven days and nights. As soon as the kiln is cooled, the lampblack produced may be taken out but that produced at the portion near the fire is not suitable for use.

Again, a similar method was described in *T'ien kung k'ai wu* 16.44 as follows:

Before chopping down the pine tree, its rosin should first be allowed to flow out, otherwise the presence of it would affect the quality of the product obtained. The method of removing rosin was to drill a small hole at the root of the tree, in which a small lighted lamp was placed and thus all the fluid rosin flowed down from the whole body of the tree to the warm place as shown in Figure 57. Then the tree was cut down and sawed into pieces of proper length to be ready for burning. The bottom of the kiln was built of brick and mud over which some round bamboo chambers were built up like the rain-shield of a boat and connected to make a length of more than one hundred and twenty feet. The

Figure 57. Method of removing rosin from a pine tree before cutting it down. Lamp burning in cavity near the root.

outside and inside of these chambers as well as their connections were strongly pasted with paper or matting. At certain intervals small holes were made for the escape of smoke (Figure 58). After the wood had been burned for several days, the kiln was allowed to cool and the lampblack was brushed and scraped out.

For making lamp-black by burning vegetable oils, the apparatus consisted of three essential parts, namely (*a*) an earthenware basin containing water, (*b*) an earthenware cup used as a lamp, and (*c*) an earthenware dish on which the lampblack was deposited.

(*a*) The basin was made of thick earthenware, round in shape, two feet six inches inside diameter and five inches deep. It had a circular rim one and a half inches wide. Beneath the rim was a hole as big as one's finger, closed with a plug of cotton. This basin

Figure 58. Making lampblack by burning pine wood.

was put on a wooden stand about three and a half feet high. Seven pieces of thin brick were placed on the bottom of the basin and around its inside, up to the rim, and a short earthen pipe with a broad rim, about nine inches inside diameter was put in the center. In the pipe also was put a piece of brick. Sometimes the basin was made of wood or stone but the arrangement of bricks and pipe was the same.

(*b*)   The cup was of glazed earthenware six and a half inches in diameter.   One of these cups was placed on each piece of brick in the basin, having been previously cleaned by scraping with a knife or bamboo stick, rubbing with the ash of rice stalk and boiling with water that had been used for scouring rice so as to get rid of all the oily dirt.

(*c*)   The dish was also made of earthenware.   It was eight inches in diameter, four inches deep, having a hollow stem four and a half inches long.   Its total height, including the stem, was seven and a half inches.   These dishes are shown in Figure 59.   Each dish was carefully polished before use, inverted and placed over the cup in such a manner that its lip was supported by the edge of the basin on the one side and by that of the earthen pipe on the other, with its central part just covering the flame of the lamp into which the cup had now been converted.

Figure 59.   Preparing dishes for collecting lampblack from the burning of oil.

The oils commonly used were *tung* oil, hemp-seed oil, wintergreen oil, rape-seed oil and soybean oil but *tung* oil gave the best result.   The oil was burned in the cup by using strips of lamp-wick grass (*Juneus communis, Juneus effusus*) each fixed on a clip as wicks.

The process of making lampblack as shown in Figure 60 is best carried out at the end of autumn or the beginning of

winter. In a closed but bright room, on wooden stands were
placed the water basins, the holes of which were toward the
outside and closed with pieces of cotton plug. Each cup
filled with oil to eight-tenths of its capacity was placed on a
brick, and was half immersed in water. The grass wicks were
fixed on clips and were put into the oil, and the dishes were
arranged in the manner
just described. Then the
wicks were lighted. At
frequent intervals the
water in the basins was
changed. After burning
more than an hour, the
lampblack produced in
the dish was swept down
and at the same time the
snuff formed at the top
of the grass was removed
by means of chop-sticks,
else, it would retard the
depositing of the lamp-
black. This operation
had to be repeated more
than twenty times every
day. From one hundred
catties of *tung* oil the
maximum yield of lamp-
black was eight taels.

*Figure 60. Preparation of lamp-
black by burning vegetable oil. The
earthenware vessels are set up on
benches in the background.*

It was said that the yield would be increased if three or four
pieces of *pa-tou* (巴豆) (*Croton tiglium*) were put into the oil.

The lampblack produced was sifted through silk gauze
into a clean and smooth jar with a small mouth. It was
finally stored in paper cases hanging under the roof in order
to preserve it from the action of moisture.

Glue was also of importance in making Chinese ink;

the use of it greatly influenced the quality of the product. That manufactured from deer horn or hide ranked first, from cow hide and fish skin next in order, and, last of all, that made from the waste of leather. Before use, it was soaked in water to soften it and then boiled with water and filtered through silk gauze or a cotton filter to obtain a clear liquid.

Drugs such as pearl powder, musk, camphor, powder of rhinoceros horn, *chin*-wood or its bark (梣木皮) (*Fraxinus pubinervus*), egg white, vinegar, bark of pomegranate (*Punica granatum* (石榴皮), blue vitriol, *tsao-chiao* (皂角) (*Gleditschia chinensis*), *ma-pien-ts'ao* (馬鞭草) (*Verbera officinalis*), *t'eng-huang* (藤黃) (*Garcinia morella*), *pa-tou* (*Croton tiglium*), etc., were also essential to Chinese ink, and used by the ancient ink-makers. Some of these were responsible for increasing the brightness and improving the color or odor of the ink and the others were used as disinfectants in order to improve its keeping qualities. When used, they were extracted by soaking and boiling in water and the decoction obtained was filtered through silk gauze to free it from impurities.

Processes—The processes of making Chinese ink consisted in several steps such as mixing, cooking, pounding, rounding, shaping, molding, and drying.

In the process of mixing, the lampblack was incorporated with the glue solution and medicinal decoction. The proportion of these ingredients, according to the *Mo ching*, was an equal weight of the black and of the glue although this was varied by some makers. The process was carried out by putting the clean black in a white porcelain basin into which the hot glue solution and medicinal decoction were poured. The mixture was quickly stirred by hand to the consistency of a thick paste without an excess of water (Figure 61). Then it was kneaded into ball-like small pieces which were wrapped in cloth and exposed to the action of

Figure 61. Mixing the ingredients of Chinese ink.

steam in a cooking vessel, which was made of wood or earthenware as shown in Figure 62. After steaming, the pieces were taken out and immediately pounded in a stone mortar with pestles, more than seven feet long, made of sandal wood (Figure 63). Half of the pounded mass was taken out to be steamed again and the pounding of the remaining half continued. This alternate steaming and pounding process was kept up until a homo-geneous and flexible mass had been obtained even though this might require seven or eight hundred or a thousand strokes with the pestle. After removing from the mortar, the pounded mass was put on the table to be rolled, still hot, into long strips which, in turn, were cut into small pieces weighing about one tael and four mace. These pieces were put into a porcelain jar covered with a piece of moistened cloth

Figure 62.   Manufacture of ink. Steaming the mixture.

Figure 63.   Manufacture of ink.
Pounding the mixture still warm
from the steaming.

or soaked in warm water for a short time in order to increase their moisture content.   Then they were taken out one by one and put on a piece of iron plate to be hammered, as shown in Figure 64. After hammering more than two hundred strokes, the coarser mass became smoother and, in turn, became harder after another two hundred strokes of hammering, and was then ready for the subsequent process.

In order to make the hammered pieces into pills or other forms to suit the mold before molding, the process of rounding or shaping was required. The soft pieces were put on an even and hard wooden table and rolled with the addition of camphor and musk. During this process an even temperature was maintained otherwise the quality of the product was affected.   Then they were twisted into pills as round and smooth as

Figure 64.   Manufacture of ink.
Hammering the mixture.

bullets or made into a
proper form with pieces
of board, one foot and
four inches long, four and
a half inches wide, and
one and a half inches
thick, as shown in Fig-
ure 65.

Finally, the shaped
pieces were molded in
wooden molds made up
from seven pieces of
wood, four for walls and
two for the top and bot-

*Figure 65.   Manufacture of ink.
Shaping before fitting into the mold.*

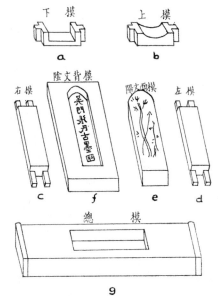

9

*Figure 66. Ink mold. a, b, c, and d,
the ends and sides;   e and f, the top
and bottom; g, the hollow block of
hard wood for holding the mold.*

tom (Figure 66). The
two latter were engraved
with inscriptions and de-
signs in relief or incised.
These were all joined to-
gether and placed inside
the seventh piece, a hol-
low block of hard wood
of such size that the walls
might be held securely
together and that the size
of the blocks of ink might
always be the same.

The ink after being
taken out from the mold
was dried on a wooden
plate known as the "ash-
pit" in which charcoal
ash was evenly spread.

The length of time required for drying in the pit varied according to the weather, ranging from one day and one night to two days and three nights.   After taking out from the pit, the pieces of ink were brushed to free them from the ash and placed on a piece of fine gauze for further drying in the air one day or two days until completely dried.   After drying they were rubbed with a piece of coarse cloth and polished briskly with wax, so as to make them clean and smooth.   Finally they were wrapped in paper to be stored up.

If the ink was made of lampblack from oil it was better to dry it in the shade or in a draft of air for a longer time as it contained more moisture.

COLORS

Through the development of the Chinese arts of drawing, painting, lacquering, the making of porcelain, etc., these products have become universally esteemed.   The beauty of their appearance depends largely on the colors, and some of these Chinese colors, either produced naturally or prepared by the old Chinese methods, have become well known throughout the world.   They are probably more beautiful and durable than the colors prepared by modern methods. However, the supply of natural colors in ancient times in China was generally confined to certain localities and periods.   For this reason, the antiquary is able to determine the period of the production of old pictures or porcelain wares by the mere observation of the colors used.   Before the T'ang Dynasty (A.D. 618–907) the colors discovered and used were few, so that only one kind of porcelain, i.e., the celadon, was known in those times.   Since that dynasty, many other excellent colors have been produced in various localities, and porcelain wares in various colors and decorations have been made.   In the Sung Dynasty (A.D. 960–1279) production was further increased, and the greatest development of the

porcelain industry took place in that period. Some of the
colors used for making pottery in the Ming Dynasty (A.D.
1368–1644) were imported from abroad, Mohammedans
transporting them into China.

In Chinese art many varieties of colors are necessary
for drawing, lacquering, pottery-making and architecture,
such as vermilion, white
lead, red lead, red iron,
ocher, copper blue, cop-
per green, Mohammedan
blue, stone yellow, purple
powder, etc. Short de-
scriptions of some of
them and the method of
their preparation follow.

Vermilion — Vermil-
ion is the most valuable
pigment produced in
China. It was early pro-
duced in a finely divided
state from the mineral
cinnabar, by powdering
and water-flotation. It
was also prepared by the
direct combination of
mercury and sulfur.
Cinnabar which occurs
abundantly in Chen chou
(辰州) in Hunan prov-

*Figure 67.   Preparation of ver-
milion by the direct combination
of sulfur and mercury.*

ince, was called *tan-sha* or *chu-sha* in ancient China and
was studied by the early alchemists as already mentioned
in detail in Chapter 2.

The old method of preparing vermilion which is still described in English or German technical books as the " Chinese
method" is worthy of mention. The process is as follows.

One part of sulfur was first melted and then mixed with four parts of mercury. This mixture was put into a small pot sealed with paper and daubed with salted mud to the thickness of four and a half inches. After drying, this pot, in turn, was put into a jar, on the mouth of which was laid an iron dish holding water for the purpose of keeping it cool. The space between the jar and the dish was also filled with salted mud. The handle was made of a strip of iron wire passing through the ear of the jar and a small hole on the side of the dish. Then the jar was heated over the fire of a charcoal stove for twenty-four hours and was taken from the stove after thirty hours. When cooled, the product was taken out to allow it to undergo the subsequent processes of pulverizing and sublimation.

The following process is also described in the Chinese Materia Medica 9.5.

Two catties of sulfur were melted in a newly made pan, mixed with one catty of mercury, and the materials were roasted together. After cooling the mixture was pulverized and put into a pot on which was placed a stone slab fastened by means of iron wire. The whole was then sealed with salted mud. Then the pot was heated over a strong fire as shown in Figure 67. After cooling, the vermilion produced was taken out. The yield was seventeen and a half taels of vermilion from every catty of mercury.

The process of clarifying the natural cinnabar, according to *T'ien kung k'ai wu* 16.41, consisted in pulverizing the mineral with an iron roller into a finely divided state, stirring it up with pure water, and allowing to settle in jars for three days and nights, as shown in Figure 68. The powder floating on the surface was decanted into another jar from which vermilion of second grade was obtained, and that which subsided was the first-grade product.

White lead—White lead, known in China under the name of *"hu-fen"* (胡粉), is also a valuable pigment. The old Chinese method for its preparation is much like the

"Dutch process" popularly used in Europe in modern times. According to the description of the Chinese Materia Medica 8.5, the process of making *"hu-fen"* is as follows.

One hundred catties of metallic lead was melted and after cooling cut into thin sheets which later were rolled into small cylinders. They were put into a wooden vat at the bottom and in the middle of which a bottle of vinegar was placed. The seams of the vat outside were daubed closely with salted mud and then papered. The air in the vat was kept warm for one week. When opened, some frost-like powder was found on the surface of the lead and might be scraped into a small jar. Those cylinders on which no frost had been produced might be left in the vat in order to undergo a further reaction and scraped again after another week. The process was repeated until the

Figure 68. Grinding and washing cinnabar.

whole material was nearly exhausted. The unaffected residues left were used as material for making red lead.

A similar process described in *T'ien kung k'ai wu* 14.22 was followed by a final operation which consisted of adding two taels of clam-shell powder to the frost produced from each piece of lead sheet and stirring together with water in a jar. After decantation, the wet white powder was dried

on paper above some ashes.   When half dried, it was cut into
pieces and after complete drying, it was stored up.

The first process mentioned above resembles the "Dutch
process" but makes no use of fermenting material for producing carbon dioxide.   Lead carbonate may have been
formed, to a less extent, by the action of atmospheric carbon
dioxide, and therefore the frost formed had to be swept away
once a week making a new contact for the air and lead so as
to promote further chemical reaction.   In the second process
carbon dioxide was produced by the action of the acid liquor
upon the clam-shells.

Other pigments—Red lead was prepared by a method
different from the present process of the direct atmospheric
oxidation of lead.   According to the Chinese Materia Medica
8.6, one catty of lead, ten taels of sulfur and one tael of niter
were taken as materials.   Some vinegar was added to molten
lead.   When bubbles rose up, a piece of sulfur was put in,
and after a short time, niter was added.   As soon as the
frothing ceased, vinegar, sulfur, and niter were added in the
same order as before.   These operations were repeated until
the red powder was obtained.   The residue left from making
white lead might be roasted with niter and alum in order to
make red lead without using vinegar.

Vinegar is assumed to take no part in the chemical reaction of the process mentioned above, because it would
vaporize or be decomposed at such a high temperature as
that of lead in a molten state.   The niter is apparently used
as an oxidizing agent by which lead is oxidized into red lead,
Pb_3O_4.   However, sulfates of potassium and lead are also
produced.   Aluminum sulfate is also present as an impurity
when alum is used.

Verdigris, known in China under the name of copper
blue or copper green, was prepared by applying vinegar to
the surface of copper sheets which were later buried in bran.
The air was kept warm and the color produced might be

scratched from the copper sheets day after day. This process of making verdigris also resembles the western method.

CHINESE STAMP INK OR *YIN-SE*

Chinese stamp ink or the red ink for seals, called *yin-se* (印色) in China, is another product peculiar to the Orient, being different from the ordinary stamp ink. According to Chinese tradition the seal for personal use originated in the last period of the Chou Dynasty and that for imperial use in the Ch'in Dynasty, thus this kind of ink may have first been made in those dynasties, even though its name and manufacturing method were probably different from those used today.

Castor oil, sesame oil, rape-seed oil and tea-seed oil were generally used for making stamp ink. Some admired castor oil but others preferred rape-seed oil. Because the former is non-drying and the latter a semi-drying oil, both are less suitable than a drying oil like linseed oil. For this reason, linseed oil has been used in modern times. Before use, the oil was boiled with the addition of drugs or exposed to the sunlight in order to improve its keeping and drying properties. The process of preparing the oil was carried on as follows.

One liter of fried castor seed was powdered and boiled in a small pan with two liters of water; the oil gradually rose to the surface. It was skimmed off into a bowl by means of a spoon. The boiling was continued until the foaming ceased; then the water was poured out and the remaining hulls thrown away. The oil was cleaned by passing through a silk filter and was boiled again in the pan until it looked like lard or goose fat. It is then stored in vessels covered with paper and exposed to sunshine occasionally.

If the addition of drugs was required, the following recipe is given in a technical book (*Wen fang ssu k'ao* 8.17–18 文房肆考):

Pai-chi (白芨) (*Bletia hyacinthina*)............ 5 mace
Ts'ang-shu (蒼朮) (*Atractylis*)............... 2 mace
Ch'uan-fu (川附) (*Aconite*)................... 3 mace
Nutmeg (肉果) (*Myristica moschata*)........ 1 mace
Dried ginger............................ 2 mace
Pepper................................. 2 mace
Kou-chi (狗脊) (*Polypodium barometz*)........ 2 mace
Arsenolite.............................. 1 mace
Tsao-chiao (皂角) (*Gleditschia chinensis*)...... 1 mace

The foregoing drugs were mixed with twenty-four taels of castor oil and boiled together in a pan until a pearl-like drop was formed on dropping the oil. After separating from the dregs, it was exposed to the sun in a porcelain jar with the addition of three mace of powdered alum and three candareens of powdered *wu-ming-i* (無名異), pyrolusite, MnO_2, until the weight of the oil was decreased to about sixteen taels.

Rape-seed oil was prepared by a similar process given in another book, *Yin wen k'ao lüeh* p. 22 (印文考略). For every catty of oil the following prescription was employed:

Pai-chih (白芷) (*Angelica anomala*)........... 1 mace
Cinnamon (交桂).......................... 2 mace
Pepper (川椒)............................. 2 mace
Pai-chi (白芨) (*Bletia hyacinthina*)........... 3 mace

After cutting into slices, the drugs were put into the oil and boiled for some time in an earthen vessel. The oil, after removing the dregs, was poured into another pan which was covered with silk waste and exposed to the sun in the hot summer until it was colorless or would not run when dropped on paper.

The oil was sometimes adulterated with white or yellow wax.

Moxa, known in China as "*ai*" (艾) (*Artemisia indica, Artemisia chinensis*, and *Artemisia moxa*), has long been used for the pad of the Chinese stamp ink. The leaves were separated from the stems and freed from dust by sifting.

After drying in the sun, the leaves were rolled up and beaten with slender bamboo sticks so as to make them soft and spongy. On grinding in a small mill, the black peel was separated and might be sifted away by passing through silk gauze. These processes of rolling, beating, grinding, and sifting were repeated a few times, until the peel was entirely eliminated. The veins of the leaves were also removed. They were then put into a small hempen bag the mouth of which was loosely tied up and boiled with pure water in an earthen pan. The water was renewed more than ten times. After boiling and pressing out the excess of water by hand, they were dried in the sun and allowed to stand overnight. They were finally rubbed on a sieve in order to ensure their being completely clean. From every catty of moxa leaves three or four mace of moxa punk were procured.

Sometimes, this moxa punk was dyed with red colors before being put into use so as to deepen the shade of the ink. One mace of the moxa punk was dyed in a bowl of the extract of safflower (*Carthamus tinctorius*) and dried in the sun. When the moisture had completely evaporated and the moxa punk became deep red in color more extract might be added and dried as before, until its color was as red as a ruby.

Vermilion before use was also subjected to a preliminary purification. It was first washed with cold water to get rid of its soluble impurities, and then pulverized in a mortar into a finely divided state. An acid solution was prepared by boiling glue and plum pulp with water, and was filtered. The clear liquor was used for floating the vermilion powder. Vermilion was gradually added to the liquor with constant stirring. After settling a little while it was decanted. This operation was repeated until all the liquor was exhausted.

The floating and decanted portions were further treated in the same way. That which floated on the surface and that which sank to the bottom were inferior but that which remained in suspension was of the best quality and of a beautiful color. This was allowed to settle and dried in the shade after pouring away the water. Then it was pulverized as before. These processes of flotation and decantation were repeated once more in order to acquire vermilion of extreme excellence.

For making the red stamp ink or *yin-se*, a certain proportion of oil and vermilion were mixed and ground together in a mortar to make them completely uniform. Then the proper amount of moxa punk was added and the whole ground together for a long time. In addition to vermilion, coral powder, pearl powder, gold leaf, mica, etc., were sometimes added to make *yin-se* of the best grade.

NATURAL DYES

The ancients preferred to use blue, yellow, and red colors for dyeing but various other colors, deep or faint, might be produced by mixing them. Before artificial colors had been introduced into China, the people always obtained their colors from natural plants, for instance, blue from indigo plant, red from safflower, yellow from different kinds of Chinese berries, etc.

Indigo—Indigo is the oldest and most extensively used blue dyestuff. It was used as a blue color at a very early time in the Orient, especially in India and China.

Although artificial, synthetic indigo has now nearly displaced the old natural product, the use of the latter still continues because of its great permanency, which is not surpassed by any other color.

Indigo occurs in nature in considerable quantities and in various species of plant, such as *Isatis tinctoria, Polygonium tinctorium*, etc., chiefly indigenous to China, India, Japan, etc.

The preparation of indigo blue was generally carried out in the 7th month of the lunar calendar. The stems and leaves of the plant were put into a pit, vat or jar according to the quantity taken. They were covered with water and pressed down by means of some pieces of wood or stone. A fermentation soon began, causing a rise in temperature. The greenish yellow liquid was separated from the plant residues, lime was added, and the mixture was violently stirred and splashed by workmen for several hours in order thoroughly to aerate and oxidize the soluble, colorless indigo white. The insoluble blue color, indigo, was precipitated, and after settling, the liquor was drained off. The precipitate was washed, filtered, and finally pressed into cakes. When used, it was mixed first with ashes of burnt rice stalk and water and again violently stirred many times.

Safflower (紅花)—Safflower is the dried petals of *Carthamus tinctorius* which contains a considerable amount of a very brilliant red color, carthamine, and was early cultivated and used in China as a drug and for dyeing. Its seeds are sown at the beginning of the first lunar month, and the plant blossoms in the summer. The flowers were collected and pounded by means of a foot-pestle. The pounded pulp was washed with water and the yellow liquor, safflower yellow, was completely removed by squeezing it in a bag. The residue was pounded and washed with sour rice soup and squeezed once more. The paste was repeatedly pounded and finally dried in the sun. It was often made into cakelike pieces to be ready for use.

Besides, the flower-buds of *Sophora japonica* or Chinese berries (槐花), red wood, and log-wood were largely used as dyes in early times.

In ancient times these natural colors were used for dyeing cotton or silk by mixing them with either soda or vinegar according to their properties; in other cases, some alum or green vitriol was added as a mordant.

Chapter 9—VEGETABLE OILS AND FATS

THE ancient processes of making vege-
table oil in China according to *T'ien kung k'ai wu* 12.64–67
embraced three different methods: pressing, boiling, or
grinding, by either of which the oil might be extracted from
its source.

Pressing was the commonest process, and was carried
out by using a very simple wooden press, which was a block
of wood about four feet in diameter and hollowed in the
middle. Camphor wood was the best for this use, and sandal
or alder wood the next, because they were strong enough to
resist the strength of the wedge-shaped wooden block which
was introduced and hammered upon. If one piece of wood
of such a large diameter could not be found, four pieces of
wood were generally joined together by iron hoops and used
instead of a single piece. The middle hollow of the press
varied in size, its capacity depending on the dimension of
the wood, ranging from less than five decaliters to one hectoliter. This hollow was made by scooping out the wood with
a chisel, making its bottom flat, and both ends oval. At its
underside were holes in which small pipes were fixed for the
flowing out of the oil.

The wedge was best made of sandal or elm wood, having
a rough surface. Both the wooden hammer and the wedge
should be hooped with iron rings so as to protect them from
breaking. The press used in the southern provinces of
China is shown in Figure 69.

The material, such as hemp-seed or rape-seed, was first roasted slowly in a pan over a mild fire, until a fragrant odor was given off. The pan used was shallow, not more than nine inches deep, having a flat bottom (Figure 70). During roasting, the seeds were agitated and turned over frequently, else the yield of oil was diminished and its quality affected.

After roasting, the seeds were ground into fine powder by means of a mill which was operated by men (or cattle) as shown in Figure 71. The ground powder was then sifted and the sifted powder was exposed to the action of steam in the cooking vat, Figure 70. After steaming, the material was taken out and bound with stalks of wheat or rice into a cake-like parcel which was later hooped with iron wires or strips of bamboo so as to fit the dimension of the press. The package was put into the press, and the wedge was inserted and struck, forcing out the oil, which ran through openings below the press into a receiver. The residue left was ground, sifted, cooked, bound, and pressed again to procure a further yield. Two-thirds of the total yield was obtained from the first pressing and one-third from the second. However, one pressing was sufficient for *tung* oil, and vegetable tallow.

In the boiling method, the materials such as castor seed or the seed of *Perilla ocimoides* (蘇蔴子) were powdered and boiled with water in a pan. The oil floated on the surface in foam which was skimmed off by means of a ladle and poured into another pan for heating over a mild fire. After the water had completely evaporated, the oil was obtained, but its yield was less than that from the other methods.

The grinding method was often used in the northern provinces for making hemp-seed oil by squeezing out the oil from the ground seed contained in hempen bags.

Vegetable tallow which has been used extensively for making Chinese candles is prepared from the seeds of *Stillingia sebifera* (烏桕), a tree growing wild and also long cultivated in China. The seeds are about as large as hazel nuts,

*Figure 69.   Press for making
vegetable oil.*

*Figure 70.   Roasting the whole
seeds and steaming the meal in the
process of procuring vegetable oil.*

*Figure 71.   Grinding the roasted
seeds.*

*Figure 72.   Grinding vegetable
tallow seeds with a foot-pestle.*

black in color, and covered with a fairly hard layer of white tallow. In order to prepare this fat, the seeds were gathered and pounded in a mortar, about two feet deep. A foot-pestle of hard stone, weighing about forty catties, fixed to one end of a lever was employed, as shown in Figure 72. The pounded mass was then exposed to the action of steam in cylindrical vessels, after which it was subjected to a gentle pressure in a wooden press like that already described. The seed itself also contains a considerable quantity of oil. By cooking and strongly pressing the finely pulverized seeds, a liquid oil is obtained, known in China under the name of "*ch'ing yu*" (清油).

For making candles, a piece of bamboo which had been boiled in water until it had swollen was split vertically into two halves which were hooped together to form a pipe. Into the pipe, molten tallow was poured by means of an iron spoon, and a piece of wick was inserted. After the solidifying of the tallow, the bamboo pipe was opened by taking away the hoop and the candle was lifted out.

Chapter 10 —INCENSE, ESSENTIAL OILS, AND COSMETICS

W E KNOW that spices were used for embalming the dead by the ancient Egyptians about five thousand years ago. Aromatic plants were probably used by the Chinese not much later than by the Egyptians. The Chinese character, 香 *hsiang*, which refers to incense, spice, or fragrance appeared very early in Chinese writing. Aromatic plants of various species were used at an early date in their raw state for flavoring purposes or burned as deodorants. From the dynasties of Ch'in and Han (246 B.C.– A.D. 220) to date, incense in various forms, such as cakes, pills, sticks, threads, or powder, has long been made by compounding different kinds of spice and used for celebrating religious rites or burning as a deodorant. In the time of Emperor Wu (140–88 B.C.) of the Han Dynasty, incense was imported as tribute and constantly used in the imperial palace. A prohibition concerning the burning of incense was given by Ts'ao Ts'ao (A.D. 155–220), the King of Wei, one of the Three Kingdoms, but he made a will bestowing his stored incense upon his concubines when he was about to die. From this, it is obvious that incense was highly esteemed in ancient times.

For the purpose of burning the incense, the burners made in various dynasties, especially in the Ming Dynasty, were elegant and delicate in various styles and are still highly valued.

The Chinese Materia Medica (ch. 14) contains fifty-six kinds of aromatic grasses and thirty-five kinds of fragrant wood (ch. 34), the majority of which are used as the principal materials for making incense. For instance, clove (丁香), anise (茴香), betany or leaves of *Lophanthus rugosus* (藿香), *Ch'en-hsiang* (沉香) (*Aquilaria agrallohca*), *kan-sung* (甘松) (*Nardostachys jatamansi*), sandal wood (檀香木), camphor wood (樟木), *lung-nao-hsiang* (龍腦香) (*Borneo, Dryobalanops camphora*), *ju-hsiang* (乳香) (*Boswellia lagbora*), *mu-hsiang* (木香) (*Rosa banksia*), etc., are largely used. The same is true of natural musk which is one of the most valuable animal products. It is produced from the preputial secretion of the musk deer, *Moschus moschiferus*, which inhabits India and Chinese Tibet.

Many recipes for preparing incense are given in Chinese texts connected with this subject.

Among the essential oils, camphor and camphor oil are worthy of mention. The tree yielding these is perhaps best known as *Camphora officinalis*, but it has been known under several other names, such as *Cinnamomum camphora* and *Laurus camphora*. The tree is distributed throughout the eastern provinces of Central China and on the island of Hainan. The crude method of preparing camphor is as follows.

The tree is felled and the young branches and twigs are chopped up and packed in perforated jars and heated over a crude steam bath. The steam enters the jars, saturates the chips, and causes the crude camphor to sublime and condense in earthenware pots placed over the jars. The crude camphor is pressed and a certain amount of oil exudes from it which is collected and is known as essential oil of camphor. Most of this oil is, however, produced by distilling the chips with water in crude stills. The crude product amounts to about three per cent of the weight of the wood used. The oil is drained from the crystalline camphor, of which it retains a considerable amount in solution. This is transferred to a still, and about two-thirds is distilled off, leaving the bulk of the camphor in the residue, which is cooled and pressed to separate out more camphor. This process is re-peated as long as it pays, and the residue forms the camphor oil of commerce.

A simpler method described in the Chinese Materia Medica 34.17 consists of steeping the chips in water for three days and nights and boiling in a pan with constant stirring. When the liquor is concentrated enough, it is filtered and allowed to crystallize. The subliming process of camphor is also described in the same book as follows. The crude camphor and earth are spread in alternate layers in a brass pan and a layer of peppermint is put above them and the pan is covered with another inverted pan. They are sealed tightly with mud and heated over a fire. The time for this process is carefully adjusted. The camphor is thus sublimed on the upper pan.

Cassia oil (月桂油) is another essential oil produced in China and well known throughout the world. It is distilled from the leaves, twigs, and other parts of the plant *Cinnamo-mum cassia*, which is chiefly cultivated in China, the chief districts being Kwangsi and Kwangtung provinces. The shrubs destined for the production of the oil are partly stripped of their minor branches and exceptionally juicy leaves during the summer months. These are conveyed in huge bundles into the valley, where they are boiled in large vessels. From the aromatic juice thus obtained the esteemed cassia oil is recovered by means of a most primitive distilling apparatus.

The distillery is located in a ravine abounding with springs which furnish an ample supply of water for coolers. An iron pan is securely placed in a brick hearth with a large fire-place; upon this pan a large wooden cylinder lined with sheet iron is placed, upon whose upper rim a large cover of strong sheet iron rests as illustrated in Figure 73. The space

Figure 73.   Apparatus for the distillation of oil of cassia.

between the cylinder and the cover, around the rim, is made tight by strips of moist cloth or rags. The distillate passes into the tin cans and the oil collects at the bottom. For each charge of the cylinder, about 1 picul of leaves and twigs and 250 catties of water are employed. The water used is mostly from earlier distillations. A single run requires about two and a half hours. The yield from a charge consisting entirely of leaves is $1^1/_2$ to 2 taels; from one consisting of 70 per cent of leaves and 30 per cent of twigs, $2^1/_2$ to 3 taels of oil. The oil obtained from leaves alone is generally superior. The quality of the oil depends in other ways upon the material submitted to distillation. Trees which are too young or too old furnish leaves less rich in oil, and large leaves are better than small, young ones. This explains the fact that the twigs and leaves gathered in spring and in winter yield an inferior oil to those gathered in midsummer and in autumn.

As to perfumery and cosmetics, rose water was imported into China in the first century. Face-powder and rouge were in use in the Chou or the Ch'in Dynasty.

Face-powder was made of white lead which has already been discussed in chapter 8. Rouge, known in China under the name of *"yen chih"* (臙脂) was prepared by mixing the juice of safflower (*Carthamus tinctoricus*) with rice powder. The method of its preparation is described in the *Ch'i min yao shu* (齊民要術), a book of the fifth century, as follows (5.17b).

The safflower was extracted with the liquor of grass-ash. The clear liquid of a beautiful red color was squeezed out from a cotton bag into a jar. This liquid was mixed with the juice of pomegranate (石榴) (*Punica granatum*) which was prepared by pounding two or three seeded pomegranates, mixing with sour rice-scouring water and squeezing through a piece of cotton cloth. Vinegar might be used instead of this juice. The liquid mixture was then added to the proper amount of rice powder and stirred violently for a long while with a piece of bamboo chop-stick. It was covered overnight, and the supernatant liquid was decanted off. The pasty residue was transferred to a silk bag and dried in the air. When it was half dried, it was pinched into small pieces as large as half a castor-oil seed and dried completely in the shade.

Because of the development of Chinese medical knowledge, the preparation of medical cosmetics, such as hair restoring oil and the various kinds of preparations used for curing freckles as well as axilla bromidrosis, etc., can be found in various old Chinese books. Many other recipes of doubtful value can also be found.

For making hair oil, some spices in addition to the medicinal ingredients were frequently steeped in the oil or in wine for later addition in order to make it fragrant. This accords with the present principles of oil maceration and alcoholic extraction. Various kinds of toilet powder, pomade, and cream were also prepared and used in China about fifteen hundred years ago.

Chapter 11—SUGARS

THE chemical term "sugar" includes a large number of substances belonging to the carbohydrates, such as maltose, glucose (grape sugar), sucrose (cane sugar), and so forth. Sugar was early known in China also under different names as *t'ang* (餳), *i* (飴), *fu* (餔), *san* (饊), *che-chiang* (柘漿), *t'ang-shuang* (糖霜), and *sha-t'ang* (砂糖). The first four, equivalent to maltose, have long been made in China by moderately heating rice with "*nieh*" (蘖), i.e., malt, and the method of preparation is said to have been discovered before the dynasties of Ch'in and Han (255 B.C.–A.D. 200).

Cane sugar, originally known in China under the names of *che-chiang* and *che-t'ang* (蔗餳) existed in the form of syrup; the former produced before the Ch'in Dynasty and the latter in the Han Dynasty. Genuine crystallized cane sugar was first made in the T'ang Dynasty (A.D. 618–907). According to the "History of the T'ang Dynasty" the Emperor T'ai-tsung (A.D. 627–644) had ordered the officers at Yang chou (揚) to offer as tribute the sugar cane from which sugar was made. *T'ang shuang p'u* 1.1 (糖霜譜) written by Wang Shao (王灼) of the Sung Dynasty also discusses the discovery of sugar-making as follows.

In the period Ta-li (A.D. 766–788) of the T'ang Dynasty, there was a monk by the surname of Tsou (鄒和尙). No one knew whence he came. He rode up San Mountain (繖山) of Ssuchuan province on a white ass to live there in a hut. When he desired provisions such as salt, rice, cabbage, etc., he listed what he needed on a piece of paper, and sent this together with the money-notes to the market by putting them on the back of his ass. On seeing this the merchant understood it and tied up the provisions as he required on the saddle of the ass and let it return back. One day, some shoots of sugar-cane of the farmer Huang living at the foot of the mountain were injured by the ass. Then Huang requested Tsou to pay him for the damage but Tsou refused and said: "Profit ten times as much as this would be obtained if you knew how to make cane sugar from the sugar-cane. May I tell you the method of preparation instead of paying you what you demand?" Huang was contented with the promise of a good result. He tried out the method and thenceforth it was introduced to the people.

THE OLD METHOD OF PREPARING MALTOSE

Maltose was early made from rice by the action of malt or barley sprout. According to *Ch'i min yao shu* (8.2a), the malting was done in the middle of the 8th month of the lunar calendar. The grain was steeped in water and exposed to the sun, keeping it moist by sprinkling with water every day until it germinated. Then it was spread on a mat in an even layer more than two inches deep and still sprinkled with water once a day until the acrospire reached the desired length. This was the green malt which was then dried to be ready for use.

For one hectoliter of rice, five liters of this malt were required. The rice was pounded, washed, and cooked. After cooling to a proper temperature, it was mixed thoroughly with the powdered malt in a pan which was put in turn into a large jar. Both the pan and the jar were covered and further wrapped with straw in the winter so as to conserve the warmth. After one day in the winter or half a day in the summer, the rice was digested and a sweet liquor was obtained. The liquor, after being filtered, was boiled with constant stirring until it was evaporated to the proper consistency.

THE ANCIENT METHOD OF MAKING CANE SUGAR

In ancient China, the principal sources of sugar were different species of cane, *Saccharum officinarum*, L., and others, of which, according to Chinese texts, some were favorable for chewing only in the fresh state and others for making sugar. The sugar cane was indigenous to Fukien and

Figure 74.   Sugar cane crusher.

Kwangtung where 90 per cent of China's total sugar output was produced.

The brown sugar (*T'ien kung k'ai wu* 6.76, 78) was made by the imperfect extraction of the juice. This was done by crushing the sugar cane in a primitive crusher which consisted of two wooden platforms six feet long, six inches thick, and two and a half feet wide, placed parallel and horizontally one above the other as shown in Figure 74. At the four corners of the platforms were inserted wooden pillars, the lower ends of which were deeply buried in the ground so as to make the whole apparatus stable and at the center of the upper beam were made two holes holding two deeply corrugated rolls of hard wood. The one was three and a half feet long and the other, five feet, protruding through the upper platform to be connected with a piece of bent wood eighteen feet long. An animal was attached to one end of this bent piece of wood and when driven set one of the rolls in motion. In this way, the cane which passed between the two-toothed rolls might be crushed, the juice running off through a trough under the crusher into a jar. The residue was crushed again. After crushing three times, the juice was largely extracted. The bagasse which was left was used as fuel. A little milk of lime was then added to the expressed juice which was boiled down in open pans until the mass began to "grain" i.e., to crystallize, and then it was emptied into tanks to cool. After cooling, the mixture of crystallized sugar and molasses was poured into conical earthen funnels, placed over receptacles, with the holes plugged with straw as shown in Figure 75. When the crystallization was nearly complete, the straw plugs were taken away and the molasses allowed to drain off through the holes of the funnels into the receptacles. The crystallized sugar was washed with water to free it from impurities. The product was quite white in the upper layer in the funnel but brownish yellow underneath. This sugar was dissolved in water and boiled with the addition of albumen, skimming off the floating scum. After it was evaporated to a proper concentration, strips of bamboo were thrown in and it was allowed to cool overnight. Larger crystals, rock candy (冰糖), were obtained in this way.

Moreover, *T'ang shuang p'u* 4 and 5, a book of the Sung Dynasty, describes the old method of preparing crystallized sugar before the twelfth century as follows.

The tools and implements used for making sugar were knives for stripping off the peel from the cane, resembling bamboo splitters, but lighter in weight; files, six inches wide, more than one foot long, for filing the cane; benches with a wooden fork at the end for holding the cane to be filed. The mill was made of two pieces of big and hard round stone, one above the other. The upper one was seven or eight feet high and more than one thousand catties in weight, and the lower

Figure 75. Crystallizing cane sugar in conical vessels from which the molasses is drained away.

one used as a base-stone had a circumference of more than ten feet. The press consisted of a cylindrical vessel made of bamboo five feet high under which was a plate and under the plate a base. On the base, at the side, stood a wooden pillar with roller and rope to tie up the pestle for pressing the crushed cane. The expressed juice was received in lacquered jars.

The process of making sugar was carried out in the 10th or 11th moon. The cane was stripped of its peel and filed into pieces as large as a copper coin. Then they were taken into the mill, the upper stone of which was turned by oxen. In other cases a mortar was used instead. The cane after being crushed or pounded was called *po* (泊) and was later sent to the press after steaming. When the juice had been extracted, it was boiled in pans and at the same time the new *po* was steamed. While the boiled juice was drawn into a jar, the steamed *po* was brought into the press. The operations of boiling and steaming were thus carried out in succession until the process was finished. After three days, the collected juice was evaporated to a proper concentration, and strips of bamboo were thrown into the jar containing it. The bagasse left was extracted with water to make a juice very suitable for making vinegar.

Two days after the juice had been drawn into the jar, the sugar began to crystallize out and small grains could be seen by testing with the fingers. Up to the first moon of the next year small crystals appeared on the end of the bamboo strips, gradually increasing in size to as large as a pea or finger, or forming groups of crystals shaped like an artificial hill. The molasses was drained off in the 5th moon, otherwise the crystals went into solution again. The product obtained was finally dried in the sun.

Chapter 12—PAPER

Before the discovery of paper the Chinese wrote on slips of bamboo or wood. The bamboo slips for writing were known as *"ts'e"* (策), or *"chien"* (簡), while the wooden slips were called *"fang"* (方) or *"pan"* (版), varying in size according to the amount of writing. In the dynasties of Ch'in and Han, pieces of silk, which were cut to any design as desired, were employed instead so as to overcome the disadvantage of the use of bamboo or wooden slips. This silk was called at that time *"fan-chih"* (幡紙), from which the present term for paper, *chih* (紙), was derived. On account of its high price, the use of silk for writing was very limited.

The discovery of real paper is credited to Ts'ai Lun (蔡倫) of the first century A.D., who offered a great contribution not only to chemical industry and the civilization of China but also to the world. According to his biography in the History of the Later Han Dynasty 108.5 and other Chinese texts, he was a native of Kuei-yang (桂陽) and first made paper from bark, rags, and fish-nets in the first year of the period Yüan-hsing of the Emperor Ho, that is, in A.D. 105, reporting his success to the emperor who was attracted by it and thenceforth the well-known "paper of Marquis Ts'ai" was popularly used.

After his invention, various kinds of fancy note paper were well known such as *shu-chien* (蜀箋), *hsüeh-t'ao-chien* (薛濤箋), etc. Tso Po (左伯) of the last period of the Han Dynasty, and Hsüeh Chi (薛稷), the Duke of Ch'u-kuo

159

(楮國), of the T'ang Dynasty were also famous paper-makers.

Hsüan-chih (宜紙) is one kind of fine Chinese paper used and valued for writing and drawing. It derives its name from being produced in Hsüan-chou of Anhui. In the era Yung-hui (A.D. 650–656) of the T'ang Dynasty, a monk lived there who first made this kind of paper, for writing Buddhist books, by using the fiber of the paper-mulberry (*Broussonetia papyrifera*) (楮樹).

Concerning the historic relation of the Chinese and the Western methods of paper-making, it is admitted that the Western method of making paper was introduced from China. According to "The Invention of Printing in China and Its Spread Westward," written by Thomas Francis Carter, the oldest paper was discovered in a ruined castle at the western end of the great wall, near Tun-huang. A great many pieces of wooden board and a few pieces of silk were also found there. Dr. A. Stein also found nine pages of a pamphlet entirely written on paper, which was supposed to be the most ancient paper so far discovered. All were sixteen inches long and nine inches wide, folded and enclosed in separate envelopes. Microscopic examination showed that they were, for the most part, made of rags. The characters written on the wooden boards were Chinese but those on the paper were Sogdian. According to the various discoveries of Chinese writing in the neighboring castles, it is conjectured that the earliest dates from A.D. 21–137 and one of them probably from A.D. 152 but there is no definite record of time on the paper itself. Thus, the last quartering of Chinese soldiers in those castles may have been in the middle of the second century and the paper found there may have been transported to the western border of China after the invention of Ts'ai Lun (A.D. 105). Again, some ancient paper of A.D. 200 was discovered by the exploring party of the Swede Sven Hedin at Lou-lan. In short, the discovery of the oldest known paper is due to the two above-named explorers.

In the fourth and the fifth century paper gradually became extensively used instead of wooden boards. As the various regions of Central Asia submitted to China at the end of the fifth century, Chinese paper was transported there for daily use. During the beginning of the eighth century, Mohammedans occupied the district, now Turkestan, and paper-making was thus introduced to the Near East from Samarkand. According to Western history, two Turkish khans struggled with each other at that time. One requested help of China, while the other asked the Arabs to support him. As a result of this battle, Chinese troops were defeated by the Arabs and the process of paper-making was practiced by Chinese workmen, the prisoners, at Samarkand.

Figure 76. Washing and steeping cut bamboo in a water pit to prepare material for making paper.

After having learned this art, the Arabs established factories at Damascus and other places to manufacture and export the paper to Europe. From Asia and through North Africa, the method was introduced to Spain, which was occupied by Mohammedan Saracens, and thenceforth the Christians gradually learned it. In 1189 the first paper factory in Europe was established at Herault in the French Pyrenees.

THE PROCESS OF PAPER-MAKING IN CHINA

The chief materials which furnish fibers for making Chinese paper are hemp, bamboo, and the bark of the paper-mulberry (*Broussonetia papyrifera*). Paper made from the last two is most common. Alum is the only form of size used in making Chinese paper.

According to *T'ien kung k'ai wu* (13.71–72), the process of making bamboo paper is carried on in the South of China, especially in Fukien where the bamboo tree is indigenous. The slender bamboo shoots make the best materials. During the summer, bamboo is cut down into pieces from seven to ten feet long which are later washed and steeped in a water pit (Figure 76). After soaking for more than one hundred days they are washed again and pounded to remove all the coarse husk and green bark. Then, the flax-like soft mass is mixed with milk of lime and put into a cooking cask (Figure 77) to be boiled over a fire for about eight days and nights. A big pan, five feet in diameter holding ten hectoliters of water is used for holding this cask. When the bamboo pulp has been cooked long enough, it is taken out of the cask and washed in a water-pit lined with wooden boards. After this, it is transferred to a strainer and strained with the addition of the hot liquor of wood-ashes. The processes of cooking and straining are repeated daily for more than ten days, until the bamboo fibers are completely soft. Then it is pounded in a mortar until it has the appearance of dough, and put into a rectangular tank filled with water. The bleaching of the pulp is sometimes done by the addition of chemicals.

The sheet is formed by the use of a rectangular hand frame, covered with a bamboo screen, and having a shallow removable ledge around the sides. This frame is submerged in the pulp mixed to a thin creamy consistency with water. When it is raised, some of the pulp is retained on it, while the

Figure 77.   Digesting the bamboo pulp.

Figure 78.   Making a sheet of paper.

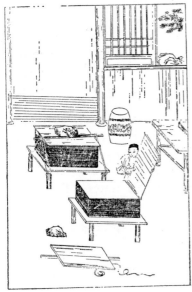

Figure 79.   Pressing paper sheets.

Figure 80.   Drying paper sheets.

water drains through. At the same time the workman shakes the frame slightly from side to side causing the fibers to form a mat of pulp on the screen as shown in Figure 78. The frame is then inverted over a piece of board, on which the sheet of pulp drops. A number of these sheets are piled one above the other and pressed heavily until the water is expelled (Figure 79). The sheets are then stripped off one by one by means of small brass pliers and dried on hot walls built of fire-bricks heated by a fire behind them (Figure 80).

Concerning the method of making paper from the bark of the paper-mulberry, the same book (13.73–74) gives the following description. For making paper, sixty catties of the bark of the paper-mulberry and forty catties of slender bamboo fibers are washed and soaked in the water-pit, mixed with milk of lime, and boiled in a pan. For the purpose of economy, straw is sometimes used instead of a part of the paper-mulberry. The bark of the ordinary mulberry tree is also used.

The well-known *hsüan-chih* is made from the bark of the paper-mulberry or of *Dalbergia hupeana* tree (檀木). In the winter, the tree is cut down and pieces of the wood are subjected to the action of steam so as to make it easy to strip off the bark. The bark is washed with water and incorporated with lime, allowing it to stand for more than ten or twenty days. When it is half softened, it is pounded with a foot-pestle, or by a machine operated by water power. The fibre is reduced to a satisfactory state of subdivision after washing and pounding three or four times. The pulp is then put into a tank for hand-made paper as already described.

Chapter 13—LEATHER AND GLUE

IT IS said that hides, feathers, and furs were used for making warm garments before the time of the Yellow Emperor. In the Shang Dynasty there were six Imperial Workers, one of whom was a Worker in Leather. Eight kinds of material including leather for imperial use are specified in the *Chou li*, about fourth century B.C. Furthermore, the method of making leather is discussed in *K'ao kung chi* (ch. 39–40), a section of the *Chou li*.

The following is a brief sketch of the native processes of making various kinds of leather in China, which are still in use in certain districts where the modern method has not yet been introduced. It consists of preliminary processes of soaking, fleshing, liming, unhairing, and deliming similar to the modern processes but with a different and simpler tanning method.

THE TANNING OF HEAVY CALF SKIN

Soaking and softening—The main object of these processes is to clear off the impurities from the surface of the raw hide (sometime impregnated with salt to preserve it) which is first soaked in a water-pit built of bricks and stones, five or six feet deep and long and three or four feet wide, for several hours. Then it is taken out and put over a wooden beam with a semi-circular surface, placed in an inclined position. The impurities on the hide are then removed by means of a blunt knife. On soaking the salted or dried hide a longer time is required in order to ensure its becoming com-

165

pletely soft. It is essential to remove all the salt from the salted hide before soaking in the water-pit. After the hide has been softened, it is put over the wooden beam to remove excess of water, blood, dirt, and other impurities.

Liming and unhairing—Lime is first slaked with water into a paste which is allowed to stand overnight or for one day and one night. After this, it is diluted with water and the milk of lime formed is poured into the lime-pit and the hides are immersed in it. The pit, built of bricks, is more than ten feet long, six feet wide, and fourteen or fifteen feet deep, being covered with bamboo matting. The milk of lime is only changed once a year, being used over and over again but from time to time fresh liquor is added to make up the necessary volume. After liming for more than ten days, the hides are taken out and unhaired on the wooden beam by means of a blunt knife.

Fleshing—The hide after being limed and unhaired is put over an inclined wooden beam of flat surface to free it from the fragments of flesh. For this purpose a sharp knife with a handle at each end is used.

If sole leather is being manufactured, the hide may be allowed to undergo the process of smoking directly after unhairing and fleshing, and no deliming is required. On the other hand, if the hides are used for making shoe leather, harness leather, or flint leather, deliming is necessary before smoking. This is done in the same way as in the manufacture of light leather to be discussed later.

The process of smoking—A rectangular stove built of bricks and mud, more than five feet wide and ten feet long is half buried in the earth, leaving only two or three feet of height above the ground. At the front end of this stove a chimney-like short pipe is built up from bricks and mud to the height of only half a foot, its diameter being about eight inches at the upper part and more than one foot at the lower part. Above the stove is placed a piece of wooden board over which mats are spread to cover the whole of the stove except the mouth of the pipe. Fuel is put into the stove through a hole at the rear at first and through the above-mentioned pipe afterwards.

After unhairing and fleshing, the hide is smoked over this stove. Straw is thrown in and fired in the stove. The workman standing by the side of the stove smokes the flesh side of the hide over the stove at a distance of more than one foot from the central part of the hide to the mouth of the pipe, whence a dense smoke issues, on account of insufficiency of air for the burning. During this time the hide is moved from side to side to ensure that it may be subjected to the action of heat uniformly, and it is sprinkled frequently with water by means of a broom, so as to prevent it from being overheated. When the hide has been smoked, it is taken off and spread out at a place far distant from the stove. Its flesh side is then sprinkled with sodium sulfate, rolled up and put aside for thirty or forty minutes. At the same time another piece of hide is smoked by the same process. When the sodium sulfate has penetrated into the smoked hide, the processes of smoking and sprinkling with this salt are repeated three or four times. The hide is then rolled up and put aside overnight. The next morning a last process of smoking is carried out without further addition of sodium sulfate. When the entire process has been completed, the hide is tied up to a wooden frame, dried in the sun, and sold as sole leather. In the making of harness leather, shoe leather, etc., the hide is spread on the ground to be half dried and then softened by hand rolling or by scraping with a brick. The details of the smoking operation may be varied so that the color of the finished product is either yellow or black. The yellow leather is made by smoking only the flesh side and brushing the grain side with pure water when it is hung up over a wooden frame, while the black is made by smoking both sides and not moistening during the drying.

THE TANNING OF LIGHT SHEEP SKIN

Fleshing—After the flesh and fatty matter have been removed from the flesh side of the green skin, it is washed with water in order to free it from all impurities.

Liming—The skin after fleshing is soaked in a lime-pit, more than ten feet deep, four feet wide, and ten feet long. The time required for complete liming varies according to the weather, and the age and concentration of the lime liquor. In warm weather, this process usually takes from five to six days, while in cold weather eight to nine days are required.

Depilation—The skin after being taken out from the lime-pit is unhaired with a blunt half-moon shaped knife. The remnants of flesh and fatty matter are completely cleaned off and the skin is reduced to a proper degree of thickness and uniformity by means of a sharp knife.

Deliming—Bate is usually used for deliming which involves the use of a fermented infusion of the dung of hens or pigeons. This infusion is made by fermenting the dung with water in a jar for from five or six days to more than ten days. When the fermentation is complete the infusion is diluted with warm water and the clear liquid obtained by decantation is used for deliming. The time of deliming varies according to the weather; in warm weather, it requires three or four days but it usually takes five or six days in cold weather.

Sodium sulfate tanning—Into a large iron pan one picul of water is poured, and ten catties of sodium sulfate is dissolved in it by heating. Fifty or sixty pieces of bated skin are then tanned in this solution for from thirty to forty minutes. Ten catties more of sodium sulfate is added and the skin is tanned again. This is done three to four times; the whole process takes six hours and uses up more than fifty catties of sodium sulfate. When the salt has completely penetrated into the fibers of the skins, they are taken out for washing and air-drying by hanging over a wooden frame to produce a kind of white leather.

THE TANNING OF FURS

The flesh side of the skin is first spread with a layer of sodium sulfate. It is folded and allowed to stand overnight. When the salt is dissolved, the skin is dried and beaten with a bamboo stick so as to free it from impurities. After trampling and rumpling it is washed in a jar with a liquor of *tsao-chiao* (皂角) (*Gleditschia chinensis*), one catty for each piece of skin. After being thoroughly washed, it is tanned with a paste-like mixture of powdered *huang-mi* (黃米) (*Setaria italica*), sodium sulfate, and water. For every piece of skin, half a catty of *huang-mi* and four taels of sodium sulfate are required. The skin is turned over with a bamboo stick three or four times every day until the chemicals penetrate completely into the fibers. According to the weather, the time for tanning varies from fifteen days to more than a month. After sufficient tanning, the skin is taken out for air-drying. By means of an iron shovel, it is made soft and even and finally the fur is combed to be ready for use in making garments.

GLUE

The ancient method of making glue, according to *Ch'i min yao shu* 9.35b–37a, consisted in boiling the animal hides or skins with water in a big pan with constant stirring, filtering viscous liquid, and allowing it to gel.

Chapter 14—SOYBEAN PRODUCTS

THREE kinds of soybean products, fermented soybean, soybean sauce and soybean curd, have been largely produced and consumed in China and Japan and exported to other countries where they are used to a smaller extent. The first kind called in China "*chiang*" (醬) or "*shih*" (豉), the second, "*chiang yu*" (油) or "*shih yu*" and the last one "*tou-fu*" (豆腐) are all considered by the Chinese and Japanese as important articles of diet. The consumption of soybean sauce is probably equal to or exceeds that of sugar in these two countries.

Both the fermented soybean and soybean sauce are made by the fermentation of either soybean alone or the mixture of soybean and wheat flour in salt solution. Their manufacture originated in the Chou Dynasty. It is stated in *Chou li* that an officer, i.e., Imperial Cook, was appointed to take charge of making and providing one hundred and twenty jars of the fermented soybean per year for imperial use. According to another book, the invention of this condiment was attributed to the Duke of Chou. The History of the Han Dynasty 91.7 and the *Shih chi* 129.15 also say that many merchants enriched themselves or obtained titles by the sale of these products in the time of the Ch'in and the Han dynasties. From this it is obvious that they were already largely consumed by the Chinese people in ancient times.

Bean curd also had its origin in early times. It is said to have been made first by Liu An (劉安) (d. 122 B.C.) and was early known as *"li-ch'i"* (黎祁): *Shih wu yüan hui* 30.6, Materia Medica 25.2.

During recent years a considerable amount of scientific investigation of soybean sauce has been carried on in China and Japan. Methods of manufacture described in early Chinese texts have been modified in many respects. The Japanese modified methods, which were developed from the Chinese, have also recently been introduced into China.

In regard to its chemical composition, Suzuki and his co-workers isolated from soybean sauce various protein decomposition products, such as alanine, leucine, proline, aspargine, tyrosine, cystine, lysine, etc. From soybean sauce, Kurono (黑野勘六) and his co-workers were also able to isolate two other compounds, one of which was an amorphous and colored substance, called "soymelanin," soluble in water, but insoluble in organic solvents, having $C_{27}H_{17}N_3O_{13}$ as its empirical formula, and capable of giving the sauce a dark brown color; the other compound which was responsible for the flavor of the sauce and named "soynal" was a compound deriving from methyl pentosan and having the empirical formula $C_6H_{10}O_2$.

THE ANCIENT METHOD OF PREPARING FERMENTED SOYBEAN

The process of making the fermented soybean consisted in subjecting a mixture of soybean and wheat flour to the action of certain species of mold and mixing and storing the product with brine in a large container to allow the fermentation to take place. The ancient method of the fifth century is given in *Ch'i min yao shu* 8.2b–7a as follows.

The soybeans were steamed in a cooking vessel for half a day. When they were cooked, the fire was extinguished but the vessel was not removed, in order to ensure that the beans were softened completely and changed to a dark color by the residual heat. After drying in the sun the mass was taken out and pounded to get rid of the skins. The processes of steaming and pounding were repeated once more. Then the material was soaked in water and cooked again. After cooling, it was mixed thoroughly with wheat-leaven (*ch'ü*), common salt, etc., and put into a jar by pressing with the hands until the mixture completely filled it up. The jar was covered with a pan and sealed tightly with mud to allow the mixture to be subjected to the action of molds present in the leaven. In the twelfth month of the lunar calendar this process required five weeks; in the first or the second month, four weeks, and in the third month, three weeks. After this, it was taken out and mixed with a certain quantity of brine. On account of the ease with which the water was absorbed by the dried bean, the brine was added to such an extent that the mixture was made as thin as congee. Then the jar was left open in the sunlight to allow the fermentation to take place and the contents were agitated by means of a paddle a few times daily for ten days, after this, once every day for thirty days. In rainy weather the jar was covered. Agitation was always required after rain. The complete fermentation always took one hundred days but after only twenty days the product was edible.

If soybeans were used alone without mixing with wheat flour, the product obtained was called "*shih*" (豉). It was better prepared in the fourth month of the lunar calendar. Rooms were built by excavating the earth to the depth of from two to four feet. Straw was best for making the roof, tiles being inferior. The windows were tightly sealed with mud in order to guard them against the wind, insects, and mice, and only a small door protected by a thick straw screen was provided for exit and inlet.

The soybeans were boiled in a large pan with pure water. After softening and draining, the mass was spread out on the ground to cool. Then it was heaped up in the room for about one day. Heat gradually developed mounting nearly to body temperature. Having been tested with the hands by stretching them into the middle of the heap, the bean was turned over by means of a rake in order to make the temperature uniform outside and inside and the heap was again made up as before. This operation was repeated after another day. If a proper temperature was maintained, the growing of the mold, which showed a faint white color, took place after four or five turnings. After the second turning, the apex of the heap was leveled down leaving a flat circular mass more than two and a half feet thick. This was further reduced to a thickness of from one and a half feet to one foot after the third and the fourth turning. During this time the white molds were produced all over the bean and gradually assumed a yellow color. The depth of the bean layer was then diminished to about five inches, and the door was kept shut for three days. The material was raked every other day into elevated rows having the depth of about four inches like furrows in the field. When the yellow mold covered the whole of it, the mass was taken out of the room for winnowing.

The moldy bean mass after being winnowed was soaked in water and beaten with a paddle so as to remove impurities and render it properly soft. It was then put into a basket and washed by pouring water over it. After draining, it was mixed with common salt and spread over a piece of matting.

A large quantity of cereal stalk which had been previously collected was now spread to the depth of from more than two and a half to four feet on the floor of a cellar which was also lined with straw. The bean was then put on to the stalks and covered with matting, above which some cereal stalks were also spread as thick as at the bottom. In summer, it was allowed to ferment for ten days; in spring or autumn, twelve or thirteen days, and in winter, fifteen days. The product—"*shih*"—prepared in this way was of a dark color, of excellent taste and fragrance.

A similar process of making "*shih*" is briefly described in the Chinese Materia Medica 25.1. Following is the translation.

One *tou* of soybean was taken and soaked in water for three days. It was washed, steamed, and spread out in a store-room and, when it was covered with mold, it was sifted and washed in water. For every four catties of the moldy bean, one catty of salt, half a catty each of shredded ginger, pepper, orange peel, thyme, and fennel, and a sufficient quantity of apricot kernel were taken. All of them were put into a jar and covered with water to the depth of one inch. The mouth of the jar was sealed with bamboo bark. It was placed in the sunlight for one month when the fermentation was complete.

THE METHOD OF PREPARING SOYBEAN SAUCE IN CHINA

Soybean sauce under the general name of *chiang yu* (醬油) or *shih yu* (豉油) is the liquid extracted from the *chiang* or *shih* and extensively used as a flavoring relish or condiment in China and Japan as before stated. The old method of making the soybean sauce which has been handed down from a very early time is still in use in China even though it is simple and crude. A modified process, however, has been carried out in modern factories.

Materials—The principal materials used for making the soybean sauce are soybeans, wheat flour, common salt, and water. The ratio of the materials used varies in different localities, the general proportions by volume being one each of soybeans, wheat flour, and common salt and two of water. The beans after being washed and soaked in water for several hours are transferred to a bamboo basket so as to drain off the excess of water. Then they are boiled in a large pan with constant stirring in order to prevent scorching. After continued boiling the material is taken away from the fire and allowed to stand for ten hours. Sometimes steaming may be used instead of boiling. The process of steaming is carried out by using a cooking pan, the mouth of which is about four or five feet in diameter. On its bottom is placed a cross-plate, above which a piece of matting is spread, and upon it is set down a cylindrical wicker cooking vessel. The steeped beans are put into this vessel and water is added to such an extent that its surface is about eight inches above the layer of beans. Then the vessel is covered, and the cover is held down by a piece of stone. After it has been cooked for about three hours, it is allowed to stand for one night.

Leavening—The leaven used in making soybean sauce is made from a mixture of bean and wheat flour. It is called "*koji*" in Japanese, corresponding to the Chinese word *ch'ü* (麴) and was known as "*huang*" (黃), yellow, in the ancient Chinese texts. It is prepared and used to ferment itself only, being different from the leaven used in making Chinese wine in that the latter is used to ferment also the other starch-containing materials.

The water is first drained off from the steamed or boiled beans by putting them into a bamboo basket. After cooling to a proper temperature they are mixed with wheat flour to a desired degree of dryness and put on matting spread over the shelves in the leavening-room, the openings of which are immediately closed. Then the mixture is subjected to the action of various species of mold and bacteria which grow up in white, yellow, green, and black colors. After about one week, the mass is turned over and the caked pieces are broken up by hand. It is finished as soon as the fungi have grown all over it. This process is always carried on at the beginning of summer or autumn.

Fermentation—Common salt is dissolved in water in a jar and the leavened or moldy mass is added to form a liquid as thick as congee. It is placed in the sunlight to allow spontaneous fermentation to take place, stirring every day and covering when it rains. Two or three daily stirrings are required in the summer but only one or two in the winter, so that the temperature may be uniform and the fermentation hastened. It will be finished in the course of from one to two years, or at least in a period of time including one summer season.

Pressing—The fermented mash is poured into hempen bags to press out the sauce. The first grade of sauce is obtained from the first pressing and the residue left may be further extracted with brine to obtain the second grade. The sauce obtained is then allowed to settle for two or three days. After skimming off the floating impurities and allowing the sediment to subside, the process is considered complete although the sauce is sometimes subjected to sterilization.

In the same way the *shih yu*, another kind of soybean sauce, is prepared in the southern provinces of China by fermenting the soybean alone without wheat flour. As the sauce produced in Kuantou (涫頭) of Fukien province has been very famous for centuries, the method of its preparation may be described.[1]

Soybeans are carefully cleaned and allowed to soak in water for about three hours. The length of time for soaking varies slightly according to the temperature. The soaked beans are then steamed for about eight hours and allowed to cool slowly. The resulting product has a pleasant odor and is dark brown in color. It is distributed in thin layers on bamboo trays which are stacked in a leavening room. The room is well ventilated in the summer and kept warm in the winter; for good results, a fairly constant temperature is required. Because of the fact that this room is generally well seeded with proper types of mold from previous use, mold growth starts on the bean very rapidly and at the end of nine days the growth is so thick that the bean cakes together and has to be stirred and broken up by hand. In

[1] *Journal of Chemical Engineering*, China, Vol. III, No. 3, 284–91.

about twelve days this leavened mass becomes quite dry, grayish white in color and is now ready for the next step of the process. During the growing of the mold heat is liberated, the temperature increases from 20° to 35° C. in the course of three or four days. By a proper arrangement for conserving the heat, the temperature of the room may be maintained several degrees higher than that of the outdoors.

The product is then transferred to bamboo baskets and immersed in running water, and the contents are thoroughly and frequently stirred in running water in order to wash off the mold mycelia. The baskets are left immersed in the water for eight to twelve hours, after which they are piled one above the other and the excess of water is allowed to drain off. Molds and bacteria that are left in the leaven again develop rapidly and a large amount of heat is liberated. Experienced workmen, by feeling the intensity of the heat generated, can judge the correct time when this step in the process should be interrupted, else the final product will have a sour taste due to the formation of an excessive amount of acid. The washing and soaking of leaven in water are peculiar to the Kwantou method, and it is believed that they vitally affect the quality of the product.

The leaven (ch'ü) or "yellow" prepared in the way described above is mixed with common salt (approximately 15–20% by weight) and placed in wooden tanks about seven feet high and five feet in diameter to allow fermentation to take place for a period of three months. In order to preserve the fermenting mash from mildew, the surface is completely covered with a layer of salt about two inches thick. At the end of the fermenting period, the liquid is drained off from a valve located near the bottom of the tank. This liquid known as "raw sauce" is light brown in color and of a peculiar odor. The raw sauce is then placed in large porcelain jars and exposed to sunlight for from two to ten weeks. A pleasant and characteristic flavor is developed after two weeks' exposure to air and sunlight. Because of evaporation of water, salt crystallizes out on the surface of the sauce in the form of scum and is removed from time to time; the resulting product is the well-known "condensed soybean sauce." The fermented mash left in the tank is extracted three or four times with strong salt solution; the first two extracts are made into a lower grade sauce, while the last extract is used again on a second batch. The residue left after the pressing of the fermented mash is used as cattle feed or fertilizer.

According to the older process already described, more than a year is required for complete fermentation, and the leaven is prepared by the growth of molds reproduced from the spores existing in the air, under such conditions that air-borne bacteria tend to cause putrefaction of the product. In order to improve these defects, about one hundred and twenty new modifications of the process have been proposed and one hundred and ten of them have been patented. Togano (栂野明二郎) in an effort to overcome this difficulty, first introduced the use of pure mold culture, *Aspergillus oryzae*. Recently, this device has been extensively used for making the leaven in all modern Chinese factories.

In order that the time required for fermentation may be shortened, the "warm fermenting process" (温醸法) has also been applied in which the fermentation is conducted at the higher temperature of 30–40° C. However, by this method the product is of a lower quality. This defect is due to the more rapid fermentation of carbohydrates at the higher temperature, the products of which hinder the progress of protein decomposition, affecting the quality of the sauce. In order to overcome this trouble, the amount of carbohydrate is lessened by omitting the wheat from the raw materials. Lacking the water-absorbing power of wheat, the omission of the latter often leads to an unsatisfactory result, the bean leaven becoming too wet. A low moisture content is favorable to the growth of molds but not to that of bacteria. Thus, if the moisture content of the bean becomes high enough to favor bacterial growth, putrefactive action takes place and the quality of the product will again be inferior. Moreover, since the products of carbohydrate fermentation are to a certain extent responsible for the fine flavor of the sauce, the omission of wheat is not justified. Togano finally adopted a method by which he carried out protein decomposition and carbohydrate fermentation separately. The leaven is mixed with an equal amount of salt solution of 20° Bé and allowed to stand with constant stirring at 42° C., the decomposition of protein being complete in twenty days. Carbohydrate in the form of partially fermented wheat is added to the leaven-salt mixture and the fermentation is allowed to continue for two more months, making a total of about three months for the entire process. In spite of all these improvements resulting in shortening the length of the fermentation period to one-fourth of what is required by the older methods, Togano's method still fails to yield a sauce that will match the delicate flavor of those produced by the older process.

During recent years, an impure amino-acid solution has been used as an adulterant or even as a substitute for soybean sauce. It is made by long boiling of the soybean press-cake with strong hydrochloric acid and finally neutralizing this with soda ash. Although the price of the sauce may be lowered by this adulteration, yet its quality and flavor are injured.

THE PROCESS OF PREPARING BEAN CURD

Bean curd or "*tou fu*" (豆腐) has been extensively used as an important article of diet from early times, but no scientific study of it had been made until the Bean Curd Company in Paris was established more than twenty years ago.

The process of preparing it consists in soaking the washed beans in cold water for seven to eight hours in the summer or a day and a night in the winter. Then they are ground together with water between two millstones into a milk-like juice flowing into a wooden tub, and then transferred into a cotton bag for pressing. The expressed juice, called "bean milk" or "bean juice," is boiled for a few minutes and drawn off into another vessel to cool. The moderately cooled juice is poured into a tub in which has been put "bitter liquor," that is, the mother liquor left after the crystallization of sea salt, and gypsum powder in order to produce coagulation. The coagulated curd together with the liquor are then poured into a square wooden tray with a movable bottom, upon which has been spread a piece of cotton cloth, with which it is wrapped. On them is placed a piece of covering board which is loaded with weights so as to expel excess of water. By this way, the soft, smooth, and white bean curd is finally obtained.

A similar process of making bean curd is also given in the Chinese Materia Medica 25.2.

From bean curd many derivative products are prepared, such as filmy bean curd, dried bean curd, fermented bean curd, etc., which are all well known.

Chapter 15—ALCOHOLIC
BEVERAGES AND VINEGAR

CHINESE alcoholic beverages, under the general name of *chiu* (酒) are for the most part of two kinds; one is rice-wine prepared from rice by fermentation, and the other is a distilled spirit generally made from *kao-liang* (高粱) (*Sorghum vulgare*). The fermenting process of the former was invented much earlier than that of the latter but it is not known when it began. The Chinese legend goes that I-ti (儀狄), the daughter of a mythical ruler, was the first one to make rice-wine. She offered it to Emperor Yü and he, after drinking it with delight, said that the throne would be lost by some future emperor indulging too freely in drink. Then the emperor separated from her and never drank wine again. However, the invention is also attributed to Tu K'ang (杜康) or Shao K'ang (少康) who lived about the same time as I-ti.

It is said that distilled spirit, called *shao chiu* (燒), *kaoliang chiu* (高粱), *paikan chiu* (白乾) was unknown in China until the Yüan Dynasty (A.D. 1279–1368), when the contact with the Western world made by that Mongol dynasty, which conquered so large a portion of Central Asia and threatened to overrun Europe, served to convey from the West a knowledge of the process of distillation.

Proof of the foreign origin of the process of distillation is given in one of the names of its product, "*A-la-ku*" (阿刺古) which would seem to be a transliteration of the Near Eastern term "Arrack." However, since the term "*shao chiu*" often appears in the compositions and poems written by scholars of the T'ang and the Sung dynasties, it is possible that distilled spirit had its origin before or in the time of the T'ang Dynasty.

The fermentation of grape wine probably began from the time of the Han Dynasty. It was said by Ssu-ma Ch'ien (163–85 B.C.) that the rich stored up ten thousand piculs of grape wine for several decades without its spoiling (123.14). But it is also stated in the Ch'ing encyclopedia that grape wine was formerly prepared in Chinese Turkestan and probably introduced from there during the Sui Dynasty (A.D. 618–906). In the time of Emperor T'ai-tsung of the T'ang Dynasty, one variety of the grape, called *ma-ju* (馬乳), shaped like the nipple of the horse, was collected and cultivated in the imperial garden and the method of fermentation was also learned. The Emperor made the wine himself and the product was agreeable.

Beer was introduced into China in modern times, during the last decades of the Ch'ing Dynasty.

In the Chou Dynasty (1100–255 B.C.), when Chinese civilization was formed, excessive drinking was common to such an extent that a prohibition order was made by the Duke of Chou, brother of the founder of the Chou Dynasty, in order to warn the people of over-indulgence. On the other hand, there was much interest in wine; for superintendents of wine making were appointed by the government; various names were given to wine; the materials and favorable conditions for making it, together with six kinds of wine-jars for sacrificial use, were discussed in the *Chou li* (周禮). On account of the development of the wine industry, the government taxation of wine was commenced in the time of Emperor Wu (140–88 B.C.) of the Han Dynasty, and has been maintained through the subsequent dynasties to the present.

We should be inclined to say that this kind of industry

is closely connected with the fate of the nation and its morality, the habits of the people as well as the financial condition of the government.   If the nation were in a state of prosperity, private manufacture would be developed and a great many people would be addicted to drinking.   On the contrary, if the nation were in financial difficulty, the rate of tax would become greater in order to increase the financial income of the government, and the private factories would thus be oppressed by the government monopoly.   Examples of the former case are not rare in Chinese history.   In the Chin Dynasty (A.D. 265–420), the Northern and Southern dynasties (A.D. 420–589), and the T'ang Dynasty (A.D. 618–907), the people from the highest rank, even the emperor, to the common class of citizens, especially the literati or scholars, almost all indulged in drinking.   For instance, Liu Ling (劉伶), Hsieh I (謝弈), Hsieh K'ang (謝康) and Juan Chi (阮籍) of the Chin Dynasty, Li Pai (李白) and Pai Chü-i (白居易) of the T'ang Dynasty were famous literati or poets but also well known as drinkers, and many books dealing with drinking were written by some of them.   Prohibition was sometimes ordered by the government with no success.

With regard to the government monopoly, it probably began in the time of the Northern Sung Dynasty (A.D. 960–1126), so that private manufacture was not permitted until the capital removed to the South (A.D. 1127).   During that time a great number of wine factories were set up in the provinces of Kiangsu and Chekiang.   To these may be traced the fermentation industry of the present time.

The ancient Chinese theory of fermentation knew nothing of mycology or of the changes through which starch is converted into sugar and sugar into alcohol.   When it was observed that the taste of liquor changed from tastelessness to sweetness and from sweetness to acridness, it was explained by no other means than the so-called "*yin*" and "*yang*" and "*wu-hsing*" or "five elements" as frequently

stated in the preceding chapters. Two kinds of important
material have long been used for making wine; one is rice
or millet, and the other is the leaven-producing yeast and
mold. The former was regarded as the "*yang*" or positive
element while the latter as the "*yin*" or negative one. The
contact of these two kinds of material to bring about fermentation was considered as being the reaction of the two elements "*yin*" and "*yang*." This was also assumed to be similar to the relation of mercury and lead in alchemy.

THE ANCIENT METHODS OF MAKING RICE-WINE

The ancient method of fermentation is described roughly
in the *Li chi* (17.20), The Book of Rites: that the favorable
time of fermentation was the beginning of the winter
(仲冬之月), the materials used were rice or millet, (秫稻必齊),
leaven, malt (麴蘗必香), and water (清必泉水); earthenware
vessels were adopted as apparatus (陶器必良); the temperature was adjusted (火齊必得) and the finished wine was
sterilized by heating (湛熾必潔). From this we can see that
the methods used more than two thousand years ago are almost similar to those of the present day. Another example
of the ancient methods can also be shown by an old tradition
as follows.

Leaves of mulberry and cooked rice were allowed to ferment with
the addition of millet or barley so as to form a concentrated mash.
This was the first process of making wine. The last process consisted in refermenting this sweet and concentrated mash with
plums and leaven nine times and the finished product was finally
decanted (*Chiu ching* 3 and 4).

By studying a valuable book, *Ch'i min yao shu*, we can
find out the methods used before or during the fifth century.
Preparation of leaven—The leaven is a kind of solid material for culturing or producing various species of fungi
including the yeasts and is one of the important materials
for Chinese wine making. Many kinds of leaven under

different names, as well as different methods of preparation, are mentioned in *Ch'i min yao shu*.[1] The following are two examples of them.

The one was called *shen-ch'ü* and was always prepared at the beginning of the seventh month (lunar calendar). Dogs and chickens were not admitted during the time of its preparation. According to the quantity, wheat was divided into three parts, two of which of the same weight were steamed and roasted, respectively, and the third one was left in a raw state. After grinding and mixing, they were rubbed into a stiff paste and then kneaded by boys into cakes each four and a half inches broad by three inches thick. A room situated at the west having the door opening toward the east was required for making the leaven. The floor was swept and upon it were placed the cakes of leaven leaving a cross-way for the passage of the workmen. Four pieces of this cake specially called *"ch'ü-nu"*, servants of leaven, were put on the floor at the four corners of the room. Then the door was closed and sealed tightly with mud. After one week it was opened and closed again after the leaven-cakes had been turned over. Still one week later they were heaped up and after the expiration of a total of three weeks they were taken out. This leaven should be crumbled finely before use.

Another slightly different process was carried out before the middle of the seventh moon and a room of any construction might be used. Equal parts of raw, roasted, and steamed wheat were mixed after the last one had been dried in the sun. With a foot-pestle they were pounded. Then they were winnowed, ground, sifted, and reground to a very fine state of division, the finer the better. *Hu-yeh* (胡葉), leaves of a kind of vegetable, were cut and boiled in water three times. After cooling, the clear liquor was mixed with the flour to make a moist mass. It was then pounded to such a state that it could be kneaded into circular pieces each of the size

---

[1] Cf. *Harvard Journal of Asiatic Studies*, 9 (1945–46), 24–44, 186.

of a large biscuit through the center of which a hole was made. These pieces of leaven were placed on the clean floor, in parallel rows leaving a cross-way for the passage of the workmen. Five particular pieces were known as "*ch'ü wang,*" kings of leaven. One of these was put in the central part of the room and the other four at the four corners. Then the door was closed and sealed tightly with mud. Seven days later, it was opened to turn over the pieces of leaven which were immediately returned to their original position and the door was closed and sealed as before. After another week they were heaped up, one heap for three *shih* of wheat and two for more and the door was closed and sealed with mud again. After a total of three weeks, they were taken out and hung up with hempen string passed through their central holes to be dried indoors for five days and finally dried in the sun.

The other kind was called *pen-ch'ü* and was also prepared in the seventh moon before or after the fifteenth according to the climate. Wheat was roasted in a large pan over a mild fire. A ladle with a long handle was tied up with rope to a large wooden pillar, in such a way that the wheat might be agitated with it quickly and constantly during the time of roasting. As soon as a fragrant smell was given out and the color of the wheat was turned yellow, it was taken out. Then it was winnowed clean and ground roughly. The flour was mixed with water and left in a heap overnight. On the following morning, it was molded into the form of cakes about fifteen inches square and three inches thick which were later trampled on by the young workmen. A hole was made in the center of each cake. Leaves of moxa which had been prepared and dried in the sun were spread over the wooden beams above which the cakes were put and they in turn were covered with a thinner layer of moxa leaves. Then the door and the window of the room were closed in order to stimulate the growth of the molds in the leaven.

After three weeks one piece was taken out for examination.
When dry throughout and mottled, the cakes were taken out
for further drying in the sun; otherwise they were kept three
or five days more. Finally, they were completely dried in
the sun with constant turning over and stored up in tall
cabinets. Every *tou* of this leaven could ferment five times
as much rice.

The preparation of wines—According to the kind of
leaven and the material used and the time of fermentation,
wines of different names and different methods of preparation are mentioned in detail in *Ch'i min yao shu*. The following are examples.

One kind was called *keng-mi chiu* (粳米) which was
made from *keng-mi*, i.e., unhulled rice, and the fermentation
was always carried out in the spring. It required one *tou* of
dried leaven, seven *tou* of water and two *shih* and four *tou*
of rice to bring about the fermentation. The leaven was
soaked in the water until froth was produced on its surface.
Dregs were removed by passing the liquor through a woolen
bag into a jar. The rice after being carefully washed and
cooked was allowed to cool. Then it was fermented with the
liquor of the leaven in the jar until it was liquefied. Refermentation was carried out twice in succession, adding eight
tou of rice each time. If the finished wine after the last refermentation were still of bitter taste, two *tou* of rice might be
further added and refermented once more.

Another kind called *liang-mi chiu* (粱米), was made
from the "high millet" or "*kao-liang,*" *Sorghum vulgare.*
Any variety might be used although the red or white was
best. The fermentation was carried on in any season. However, in the spring or autumn the leaven used was rasped
finely but in the winter it was pounded and sifted into a fine
powder. In general, one *tou* of the leaven was required for
six *tou* of the millet and one *shih* of the millet needed three
tou of water. According to the weather, the leaven was

either soaked in cold water and filtered from its dregs or soaked in a cooled and thin congee of *kao-liang* and used without filtering. The millet was divided into three equal parts, one being used for each time of fermentation. The cooked millet after being spread out to cool to body temperature was put with the leaven into a jar which had been previously heated by steaming and wrapped with straw. The mixture was agitated by means of a paddle. The jar was then covered with an inverted pan and sealed with mud to let the contents undergo fermentation for one night in summer, two nights in spring or autumn, or three nights in winter. After the millet had been liquefied, refermentation was twice carried on by the same process. Ten days after the end of the third refermentation, the wine was pressed out, being as white as silver. It might be as aromatic as ginger or cinnamon, as sweet as honey, or as bitter as bile according to the success of the process. This method as a rule produced wine more fragrant, stronger, and superior to any other.

From the above we come to the conclusion that cleanliness was already observed by the ancient people in order to preserve the leaven from too much growth of bacteria, and that the temperature of preparing the leaven and of conducting the fermentation was maintained or adjusted by various means, such as the closing and opening of the room-door, heaping and turning over the leaven, warming and wrapping the fermenting jar, etc., and that refermentation was regarded as a very important process in the ancient methods of wine-making. The last is in some respects equivalent to the culture of yeasts, and is like the present-day method of making Shao-hsing wine (紹興), a very well-known rice-wine today in China, which will be discussed later.

Further reference to the ancient method of wine-making in the eleventh or the twelfth century is found in two ancient books, under the same name of *Chiu-ching*, Wine Classic. One of them, known as *Tung-p'o chiu ching*(東坡酒經),

written by Su Shih (A.D. 1036–1101), a very famous Chinese literatus of the Sung Dynasty, describes the important method of wine-making in ancient times although it contains only a few hundred words. It is now translated as follows (ch. 1.7).

The southern people prepare the *ping* (餅), medical cakes, by mixing the *no-mi* (糯), glutinous rice, and *k'ang* (秔), non-glutinous variety of rice, with the vegetable drugs, and the finished product is excellent if it has fragrant flavor, acrid taste, and is light in weight. After mixing with the juice of ginger and steaming, the flour dough is hung up by means of a string and dried in the air, the longer the time the greater its strength. This forms the *ch'ü* leaven of best quality. Five *tou* of rice are now taken for illustration. It is divided into five parts, three *tou* for one part and five *sheng* each (ten *sheng* make one *tou*) for the other four parts. The first one is used for the first fermentation and the other three for three times of refermentation, the last one being used to be fermented with the wine-lees. Four taels (about 31 grams per tael) of the *ping* are required at the beginning of fermentation and three taels of *ch'ü* for each refermentation. Both the *ping* and the *ch'ü* are moistened with a small amount of water before use in order to mix uniformly with the rice. The fermentable materials are put together in a jar and at the central part of the mixture a well-like concavity is made, from which liquid will overflow in a few days. This is the beginning of wine production. During this time a vigorous fermentation is carried on and the taste of the liquid is slightly bitter. It is finished after three refermentations. Because the property of *ping* is stronger and that of *ch'ü* is weaker, the workman should frequently test with his tongue so as to judge the proper amount of the material required. Three days after the overflowing from the well-like cavity, it is successively refermented three times in the course of nine days, making the entire process of fifteen days. When finished, one *tou* of boiled and freshly cooled water is added. It is customary in Yenchou (炎) to use water that has been boiled and cooled for each fermentation and refermentation. Five days after the water has been added, three *tou* and a half of wine may be strained out. This is the concentrated product. Half a day before the process of straining, the rest of the rice is boiled into congee by adding three parts of water to one part of rice. It is then mixed with a total of four taels of the *ping* and *ch'ü* together with the *tsao* (糟), wine-lees or the mash of fermenting grain after straining away most of the wine, and refermentation allowed to go on for five days. One *tou* and a half of wine is again pressed out, being a comparatively diluted product. The first and second products are put together to make the total yield of five *tou*. For drinking, it is delicious and strong after storing for five days. The fermentation of congee must begin just at the time when the process of straining is being finished; otherwise the *tsao* will be quickly dried in the air, affecting the property of the finished product. If the fermentation takes a longer time, the wine produced will be stronger in property and greater in amount and vice versa. For this reason, it generally takes thirty days for the whole process.

The use of the "*ping*" was peculiar to this process, from which, it is said, the present method of making Shao-hsing wine by the use of "*chiu-yao*" (酒藥), wine medicine, is derived. Besides, the refermentation was also regarded as an important process in those times.

A more particular description of this subject is given in another book called *Pei shan chiu ching* (北山酒經), published in A.D. 1117, the author of which was Chu Hung (朱肱), otherwise named Chu I-chung (翼中) or Chu Ta-yin (大隱), a hermit of the Sung Dynasty, who retired in his youth and lived at the beach of West Lake in Hang-chow of Chekiang in his old age. According to this book, there were three main kinds of leaven, which were either prepared in a closed room or in a draft.

Many recipes for making them are given in the book and the following are examples.

One *shih* of wheat was milled into sixty catties of white flour which were distributed on two bamboo trays and mixed with seven *sheng* of a decoction of *she-ma* (蚍麻), probably *Humulus lupulus*, and the following medicines.

Pai-shu (白朮) (*Atractylis*)........................	$2^1/_2$ taels
Ch'uan-hsiung (川芎) (*Conioselinum univittatum*)....	1 tael
Fu-tzu (附子) (*Aconitum fischeri*).................	$^1/_2$ tael
Peduncle of melon (瓜蒂)........................	1 piece
Mu-hsiang (木香) (*Rosa banksia*).................	$1^1/_2$ mace

The above medicines were pounded and sifted into a fine powder with which sixty catties of flour were thoroughly mixed.

Sixteen catties of *tao-jen t'ou* (道人頭) (a kind of grass) and eight catties of *she-ma* were cut and pounded into pulp which was macerated and agitated in a pan with freshly drawn well-water. Then the mixture of flour and medicines was thoroughly mixed with one *tou* and four *sheng* of this liquor.

The process of mixing was carried on to get a mass having a favorable degree of dryness, sticking to the hand on grasping and not scattering when loosened. After passing through a coarse sieve it was thickly covered with heat-insulating material in order to conserve the temperature for six or eight hours, and then put into the molds and wrapped with cloth before trampling to a state of firmness.

A clean and quiet room was previously prepared for use. Wooden boards were placed upon the floor; over the boards, wheat stalks were spread about one foot thick, above them the mats, on which the pieces of leaven were laid. They were then covered with stalks and an upper layer of leaven was arranged in the same way. At the four sides were also stalks in order to prevent the access of air and the top was covered with straw as well. The cakes of leaven were examined twice a day; if too hot, their central part turned red and if too cold they did not decrease in weight. In the former case some of the covering was taken away so as to allow the access of cold air. After four to six hours or more than half a day they were covered again as before. If, on the contrary, the temperature was too low, more stalks should be used for the covering. More than ten days later, every piece of leaven was allowed to stand up and was placed in such a way that one was opposite to the other. They were again covered as before until the process was completed. When finished, they were taken out for use.

Examples of those kinds of leaven which were prepared
by hanging in a draft are shown below, and the following
drugs were used.

Mu-hsiang (*Rosa banksia*)	3	taels
Ch'uan-hsiung (*Conioselinum univittatum*)	6	taels
Pai-shu (*Atractylis*)	9	taels
Fu-tzu, white (*Aconitum fischeri*)	$^1/_2$	catty
Kuan-kuei (官桂) (*Cinnamonium cassia*)	7	taels
Fang-feng (防風) (*Peucedanum rigidum*)	2	taels
Fu-tzu, black	2	taels
Peeled peduncle of melon	$^1/_2$	tael

The above were pounded and sifted into fine powder
before mixing thoroughly with a total of three hundred
catties of powdered *no-mi*, glutinous rice, and white flour.
Again, two catties of apricot kernels from which the peel
and apex were removed, were pounded to a pulp in an
earthen pan; then one catty each of *liao Polygonum* (蓼)
and *she-ma* and half a catty of *tao-jen-i'ou* were added and
pounded with the apricot kernel pulp. This mixture was extracted with five decaliters of freshly drawn well-water to
obtain a concentrated liquor, which, in turn, was added to
the mixture of rice, flour, and drugs in a pan, mixing thoroughly by means of the hands. This wet mixture was then
heaped up on a clean mat and covered overnight. On the
following morning, it was put into molds and trampled to
firmness. The pieces formed out of the molds were wrapped
in straw and each put into a paper bag and hung in a draft.
After half a month, the wrappings were taken away, but
the pieces of leaven were left in the bags for two months
more.

Another similar process consisted in mixing two catties
each of *liao*, *she-ma*, and *ts'ang-erh* (蒼耳) (*Xanthium stru-
marium*), and one catty each of *ch'ing-hao* (青蒿), *Artemisia
apiacea*, and mulberry leaves. The mixture was smashed
in a stone mortar, squeezing out the juice through a piece of

cloth. One hundred pieces of apricot kernel, having the peel and apex removed, were finely pounded and added to the said juice. One *tou* of *no-mi*, glutinous rice, after winnowing, washing, and drying, was ground into a fine powder which was further dried in the sun to a desired degree of dryness. This powdered rice was then added to the above mixture and the whole was kneaded into cake-like pieces each of which was coated with the powder of the old leaven and placed on the sieves. Previously, dried straw was spread on the floor to the depth of about four and a half inches in a tightly closed and clean room. Sieves were now placed on the straw and covered with an even layer of grass to a depth of more than six inches. The cakes of leaven were examined from time to time within one or two days by stretching in the hand. When the cakes were moderately hot and the inside had a mottled appearance, the covering was taken away. On the next day, the cakes were taken out of the room and put on a table in a draft for drying. When partially dried, they were taken off, one by one, from the sieves and put into the baskets which were hung in a draft. They were brought into use after one month.

With regard to the process of wine-making the same book (*Pei shan chiu ching*) gives the following descriptions.

Preparation of sour liquor from rice or millet—On the hottest day of the sixth moon, one *tou* of wheat was boiled with water to make congee. The vessel containing it was loosely covered in the daytime and tightly at night. It was warmed every day until it was sour enough in taste to be ready for use. This sour liquor was of great importance in making wine. Another method of preparation consisted in mixing water and vinegar and boiling them with the addition of onion, pepper, etc. This was known as "new sour liquor." A third method was to dilute the water used for scouring rice and boiling it with the same ingredients as just specified; this was known as "old sour liquor." Both of these were used, but were inferior to that prepared by the first method.

Boiling the sour liquor—The sour liquor made in the sixth moon was kept boiling for some time. The white floating foam was skimmed off by a bamboo skimmer, and the boiling continued. Then one bundle of onion, one tael of pepper, two taels of oil, and one cup of flour, which had been previously mixed with half a bowl of the liquor, were added and boiled with constant stirring. The onion and pepper were filtered off when the former had softened. If the liquor was too sour, it was diluted with a certain amount of water; if not sour enough strong vinegar was added.

Warming the rice—This process consisted in mixing raw rice with the warm sour liquor in a jar, stirring up and down from three to five hundred times by means of a paddle. The operation varied according to the age of the rice. New rice was added to the liquor and the process was called "inverse warming," but old rice, on the contrary, was sprinkled with the liquor and known as "right warming." Each operation was carried on daily, one night being sufficient in the summer but two days or three nights in the spring or winter. Irrespective of the time required, the rice was taken out as soon as the consistency of the liquor was like cow's saliva and the grain was sour enough. This was known as "sour rice."

Cooking the sour rice—The sour rice, after being taken out of the liquor and having the water drained off through a jar-filter, was cooked in portions large or small according to the capacity of the cooking vessel. Another portion of sour liquor was diluted with water and boiled with the addition of onion, and pepper as above mentioned. After cooling, it was used for sprinkling the cooked rice, two *tou* being required for one *shih* of rice. The cooked rice was then beaten by means of a paddle so as to break the grains completely.

Fermentation—The cooked rice was spread on a table and turned over frequently in order to make it extremely cool or moderately cool or at about body temperature according to the weather. Then it was mixed thoroughly with the leaven and put into a jar for fermentation.

The property of the finished wine depended on the amount of the leaven used as well as on the size of the pieces. One-tenth of the amount of the rice was the amount usually favored; if more or less than this was used, the wine tasted bitter or sweet but could be blended as desired. The size of the pieces of leaven was varied according to the time of fermentation. In the spring or winter, on account of the longer time of fermentation, the leaven used was in pieces as small as dice; while in the summer, the time was shorter and the leaven used was in still smaller pieces. In short, the finer the leaven used, the sweeter the wine produced; and conversely, the coarser, the more acrid.

The bottom of the jar was covered with the powdered leaven, four or five taels being left for a topmost layer. The cooked rice after being cooled to the proper temperature was put into the jar, layer by layer, each addition being followed by pressing along the sides of the jar with the hands and finishing by making a concave hollow in the middle part of the rice. The whole was then covered with the remainder of the leaven. From three to five or more *sheng* of moderately warm water was poured into the hollow and sprinkled on the surface. One or two days later, if there was not much water in the cavity, the whole jar was wrapped with a mat. While on the other hand, if the fermentation had proceeded to such a degree that a great amount of water came out of the rice and overflowed from the hollow, the rice was stirred by means of a paddle and the jar covered. After three days it was agitated up and down once more. This fermented liquor was known as "mother of wine" and was ready to be used for refermentation.

Cooking the rice for refermentation—More rice was steeped and washed before putting into the cooking vessel for steaming. During the process of steaming, the rice was sprinkled frequently with hot water and agitated with a bamboo rake to make it homogeneous, soft, and of a proper consistency. Then the cooked rice was transferred into a pan, sprinkled with hot water, and covered with another vessel. After a short while it was spread on the table and turned over two or three times until it was cold.

Refermentation—This process was known as *"t'ou-ju"* (投醹) in the original book, *Pei shan chiu ching*, and consisted in refermentation of the "mother of wine" and cooked rice. It was very important to carry it out at a favorable time, neither early nor late. The cooked rice was added while the "mother of wine" was frothing rapidly and of sweet taste. Then the fermenting jar was covered with straw in cold weather, with a mat in warm weather, or with a cloth only on hot days. The fermenting mash was agitated daily up and down with the hands so as to make the temperature uniform. During the cold season the workmen's hands and arms were washed with hot water before agitating, but on warm days the agitation was done with a wooden paddle. This operation was continued for five days. In spite of the liquefaction of the rice, it was advisable to carry out a further fermentation by the addition of more cooked rice if the evolution of the gas bubbles was still rapid and the leaven strong enough. If the fermentation became slow, the jar was closed and sealed tightly with mud for more than ten days in the summer, forty days in the winter and twenty-three or twenty-four days in the spring or autumn before pressing.

Pressing and pasteurizing—Cloth bags were filled with the refermented mash and subjected to pressure between wooden boards. The pressed wine flowed into a jar which conserved its flavor and bouquet. The jar was covered with straw or wheat stalks but a piece of cloth was used instead in warm weather. After three or four days, the clear liquor was decanted and poured into bottles.

The process of pasteurization was carried out by steaming the bottled wine in a cooking vessel until a peculiar odor was noted and the wine overflowed out of the bottles. Then the vessel was uncovered and taken away from the fire. The bottles were taken out after cooking, sealed, and buried in lime to settle.

Chu Hung has left us a vivid description of the processes of wine-making in the twelfth century as above mentioned. The following flowsheet will make the whole process clear:

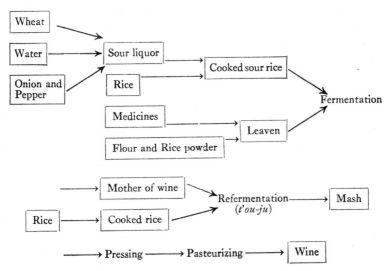

Moreover, from the foregoing description, we may make the following conclusions.

1. The leaven used in ancient times consisted of glutinous rice or flour mixed with many kinds of medicinal herbs some of which are still used in compounding the so-called *chiu-yao*, wine medicine, for making Shaohsing wine and which probably stimulates the growth of fungi.

2. The use of the sour liquor is most peculiar to the ancient process from which the present method of making

Shaohsing wine by using the sour liquid obtained by steeping rice in water indeed originated. From the viewpoint of modern scientific principles, this liquor, being acid in property, capable of retarding the growth of bacteria and favoring the reproduction of yeast, is truly beneficial to fermentation. The use of lactic acid in modern processes of alcohol manufacture was unknown in Europe a century ago but the Chinese knew how to use sour liquor (containing a considerable amount of lactic acid) for making wine nearly a thousand years ago.

3. It seems that the process of refermentation was essential in the ancient method as it is often discussed in ancient books about wine. This accords with the modern process in assisting the propagation of yeasts and in improving the flavor of the finished wine.

4. The method of pasteurization was, indeed, invented at least eight hundred years ago in China, being about six hundred years earlier than the experiments of Abbé Spallanzani (A.D. 1765) and about seven hundred years before the discoveries of Louis Pasteur (A.D. 1860).

THE ANCIENT METHOD OF MAKING DISTILLED SPIRIT IN CHINA

The ancient process of distilling spirit is described in the Chinese Materia Medica 25.14 as follows.

Concentrated wine was put into a colander together with the wine lees, and distilled, the vapor on condensation being received into another vessel. Damaged or sour wine might also be distilled.

Again, any kind of rice was cooked either alone or together with wheat and allowed to ferment in a jar for seven days. The wine produced after fermentation was distilled to produce a spirit as clear as water and of a strongly pungent taste. The distilling apparatus used in ancient times is shown in Figure 81.

THE MODERN PROCESSES OF MAKING RICE-WINE, SHAOHSING WINE

Of the various kinds of Chinese rice-wine, Shaohsing wine is the most famous. It has been produced in large quantity annually at Shaohsing in the province of Chekiang, and derives its name from that place. Rice-wine produced in other places in China is known under the general name of "*huang chiu*," yellow wine. The following is a brief sketch of the processes of making Shaohsing wine.

Materials—The principal materials are rice, water, "wine-medicine" (*chiu yao*), and "wine-leaven."

The rice used as the essential material is *no-mi*, glutinous rice, which, for the most part, comes from Wu-hsi, Tan-yang, and other places in Kiangsu and Chekiang provinces. At first, the unhulled rice is pounded fine in order to get rid of the outer coat and leave the endosperm; the bran is fanned away. It is then steeped in water in jars each of

Figure 81. Ancient still for making spirits. The workman is pouring water into the reservoir which cools the still-head.

which holds one *shih* and five or six *tou* of rice. The surface of the rice is covered with water to a depth of from four to seven inches, varying the soaking time from thirty-six to forty hours according to the quality of the rice and the temperature of the water used. The quality of the wine produced depends largely upon the quality of the rice employed. The workmen in Shaohsing are so experienced that they can judge the quality of the rice at first sight. The steeping water (known as *chiang*) (漿) is drawn off by means of a pump or rattan drainer and the rice is washed with pure water two or three times before cooking. The cooking process is carried out by distributing the rice in each jar into three cooking vessels each having a perforated bottom upon which is placed a round mat, made of palm hair. The rice is steamed for more than one hour.

The properties of the wine produced likewise depend on the water used for fermentation. The high reputation of Shaohsing wine may be partially accounted for by the good quality of the water which is collected from Lake Chien (鑑), River Hsia (霞), River Jo-yeh (若耶), and other places near Shaohsing. These streams are derived from sources in the mountains and valleys, flowing and passing through earthy, sandy, and rocky strata. They have a moderate hardness and contain no injurious matter, being clear, odorless, tasteless, and very suitable for steeping, washing, and fermenting.

The "wine-medicine" corresponds to the "*ping*" in *Tung-p'o chiu ching* or the "*ch'ü*" in *Pei shan chiu ching* both of which have been already described. It is made of rice powder and many kinds of vegetable drugs. It contains a great many species of fungus, such as yeasts, especially *Saccharomycetes*, *Shaohsing*, and molds, *Rhizopus*, *Monilia*, *Aspergillus*, *Absidia*, etc., which are all capable of growth and reproduction when a small quantity of "wine-medicine" is introduced into the fermentable material. Fermentation in the substance on which they act is due to the enzymes which they secrete.

There are two kinds of "wine-medicine," black and white, square, round, or oval in shape, with the same power of fermentation. The white kind is prepared as follows.

During the summer, the wild cultivated *liao* (*Polygonum*) is plucked before it has blossomed. After drying in the sunlight, the stalks are cut off and the leaves pulverized into fine powder. At the beginning of the eleventh moon, this vegetable powder is mixed thoroughly with the fresh juice of *liao* and rice powder. The favorite ratio is one part of vegetable powder to ten parts of rice powder with enough juice to make the mixture stiff. This mixture is then molded, trampled on, and cut into pieces slightly larger than one and one-half inches square. These are coated with the powder of old "wine-medicine" and rolled on a board into ball-like pieces. They are then placed on straw mats and covered with straw and hempen bags. Having closed the room for one day or more, the white mycelia of the fungi gradually appear on the surface of the pieces. Then the covering may be taken away and they are placed on shelves to be turned over once or twice daily in order to keep the heat developed by the physiological action of the micro-organisms uniform. During fine days, they are given a drying in the sunlight. They are pulverized before use in the winter.

A similar process is used for preparing the black "wine-medicine" but more varieties of plants are needed for its preparation, such as *ch'en-p'i* (陳皮), peel of *Citrus, hua-chiao* (花椒) (*Zanthoxylum bungei*), *kan-ts'ao* (甘草) (*Glycyrrhiza glabra*), *ts'ang-shu* (蒼朮) (*Atractylus ovata*), etc.

The "wine-leaven" is another kind of fungus-producing material, also essential in Chinese wine-making. Many species of molds, such as *Mucor, Rhizopus, Absidia, Aspergillus, Monascus*, are present in it. The molds are active in converting starch into fermentable sugars by the action of such enzymes as diastase which they secrete; and then the yeasts which occur in the "wine-medicine" are responsible for causing an alcoholic fermentation. For this reason, the "wine-leaven" used in Chinese wine-making functions as malt does in brewing.

Both wheat and barley are used as materials, but the former more commonly. Sometimes, both of them are mixed for use in the proportion of two parts of barley to eight parts of wheat.

The process of preparing the leaven is carried out at the beginning of winter. Prior to this time the grains are winnowed and milled into flour. A rectangular room is used for making the leaven, having a dry and clean floor, eight to eleven feet long and varying in width according to the amount of leaven to be prepared. The walls are surrounded with straw mats so as to conserve the room temperature, and at the upper and lower sides are the windows with wind-shields for convenience in regulating the temperature and ventilation. The central part of the floor is spread with straw to the thickness of one foot and three inches, and on it, are put bamboo mats. This is called "the leaven bed."

Two buckets of flour (about twenty or twenty-five kilograms) are mixed thoroughly with more than five liters of pure water. The dough is then put into a wooden frame, the bottom of which is movable. It is covered with a straw mat and trampled on to make the dough cake into one piece. After this, the mat is taken away, and the dough is taken out and vertically shredded with a knife into four strips, each of which is, in turn, horizontally cut into pieces known as "leaven-piece" about two and a half feet long and seven inches thick. Two pieces are bound together with rope to form a "leaven-parcel" which is later transferred to the "leaven bed" by means of a small paddle. While the windows of the room are closed, the molds gradually develop and the temperature of the room also rises. The windows are half open if the temperature is too high. After three or four weeks, the reproduction of mold is nearly complete and the leaven obtained is of a yellowish white color, fragrant smell, and sweet taste. Then it is taken out and stored up until needed in another room which is well ventilated and has the proper degree of humidity.

Fermenting processes—The process of fermentation is

carried on in two stages, a first fermentation and a secondary fermentation, the latter, of course, equivalent to the refermentation in the ancient process.

In the first fermentation the "mother of wine" is produced, and the yeasts are well cultured and propagated in a liquor which is used in the subsequent process. One *shih* and six *tou* of fine rice are treated as described in an earlier paragraph. After the rice has been cooked in a vessel with a perforated bottom, the vessel is placed over a wooden bucket and cold pure water is poured on and passes through the rice and drains down into the bucket. By this means, the temperature of the rice drops quickly and the water which becomes rather hot after draining may be scooped with a wooden ladle and poured through again until half of the quantity of draining water has run through and the proper temperature of the rice (about 30° C.) has been acquired. After the water has been completely drained off, the cooked rice is transferred to the fermenting jar. A small quantity of "wine-medicine" is added and mixed with the cooked rice and finally a concavity is hollowed out in the central part of the mixture. The jar is wrapped in heat-insulating material so as to maintain the temperature of the contents at about 30° C. The grains gradually liquefy, losing their stickiness and becoming completely soft in from twenty-four to forty-eight hours. The liquor produced in the central hollow is of sweet taste due to the saccharification of the starch by the spontaneous growth of the molds present in the "wine-medicine." This is therefore called "sweet liquor." Then, one hundred and seventy or eighty catties of water and four *tou* (about thirty-two catties) of "wine-leaven" are added and mixed thoroughly by agitating with a long paddle. The jar is now covered and wrapped with straw. After closing the fermenting room, the room-temperature will gradually rise to as high as 30° or 40° C. in the course of time, that is, in from one day and one night to three

or four days. To prevent the temperature becoming too
high, some of the cooked rice floating on the surface should
be pressed down and the remainder agitated up and down
from time to time with a wooden paddle. This operation
known as "*k'ai-pa*" (開耙), "opening with the paddle," is
carried out from three to six times every day. The temperature should be kept about 30° C. From the beginning of the
operation "*k'ai-pa*," the sweet taste of the liquor gradually
becomes pungent, the percentage of sugar and dextrin de-
creases and that of alcohol increases day after day. This
stage of fermentation, i.e., the first fermentation, is accomplished in two weeks. Although the product may sometimes
be taken as a drink, yet it is still stored, for the most part, in
the jar as material for the following fermentation.

The secondary fermentation is carried out for the purpose of obtaining a stronger and more delicious liquor, the
renowned Shaohsing wine. The "mother of wine" produced
by the foregoing process is mixed with cooked rice, "wine-
leaven," pure water, and sour steeping water to bring about
a fermentation, the proportion of the materials used being
varied as desired or according to the condition of localities.
An illustration is given below.

One *shih* and eight *tou* of glutinous rice (about one hundred and seventy catties), four *tou* of "wine-leaven" (about
forty catties), seventy catties of "mother of wine," three
buckets of rice-steeping water (about one hundred catties),
and four buckets of pure water (about one hundred and forty
catties) are mixed to bring about a fermentation. At first
the pure water is poured into the fermenting jar and then the
cooked rice is added and agitated with a paddle, followed
by the addition of "mother of wine," "wine-leaven," and
rice-steeping water with stirring in order to render the stiff
mass uniform. If the weather is not cold, covering is unnecessary, otherwise the jar is covered and wrapped with
hempen bags and straw as in the case of preparing "mother

of wine." Then the fermentation takes place rapidly with rise of temperature and evolution of gas bubbles. Workmen of much experience watch it constantly and decide the proper times to "*k'ai-pa*," from the maximum of more than ten times to the minimum of three times daily according to the temperature. At first the temperature is above 30° C. but

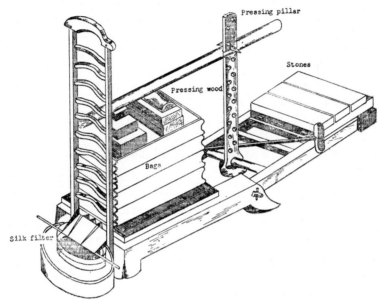

Figure 82. Wine press for separating rice wine from the fermented mash.

gradually it drops as the fermentation slows down, and then the frequency of "*k'ai-pa*" may be diminished. This fermentation lasts about one week and the fermented mash is either drawn off into large earthen containers or still left in the original jar to undergo further fermentation.

Pressing and decanting—After seventy or eighty days, when the entire process of fermentation has finished, all sediment and precipitate in the mash are removed by pressing and decanting. The mash is first introduced into silk bags more than four feet long and six inches in diameter, the mouths being bound with bamboo leaves. A hundred or more of these bags filled with mash are piled up on the press (Figure 82). By the weight of the bags and of their contents above, the wine is pressed out from the lower bags and runs into a jar. As soon as liquid no longer drips, blocks of wood are placed, one after another, on the topmost of the bags. The lever is then brought into action and heavy stones are hung up on the other side of the pressing pillar to increase the weight employed. This process occupies about ten hours, by which time the wine will be completely pressed out. Then the residue is taken out of the bags which, in turn, are filled with new mash and pressed again. The pressed wine is allowed to settle in another jar for a few days in order to let most of the suspended matter deposit. Then it is decanted. The settlings are mixed with the new mash and pressed again.

Pasteurizing—The finished wine is pasteurized by heating in order to improve its keeping property. This process is carried out by first heating the wine in an open pan to 50–60° C. and skimming off simultaneously the coagulated protein by means of a bamboo ladle. It is then gradually heated until it boils and then instantly drawn off into earthen containers which have previously been sterilized by steaming and dried by rubbing. The mouths of the containers are covered with bamboo leaves and sealed with mud. Then they are stored by piling up in a room for months or years, the longer the better.

THE MODERN PROCESSES OF MAKING DISTILLED SPIRIT—*KAO-LIANG* WINE

The process of making *kao-liang* wine consists of three stages, namely, preparing the leaven, fermentation, and distillation.

Preparing the leaven—The materials and their proportions vary in various localities. Barley and small peas are, for the most part, used, and *ch'iao-mai* (蕎麥) (*Fagopyrum esculentum*) is sometimes used for cheapness instead of barley. The proportion is nearly in the ratio of one *shih* of barley to two or three *tou* of small peas. Both of them, after being mixed, are crushed into powder, mixed with water, using two *sheng* or more and molding to form brick-like pieces. These pieces of leaven are then heaped up in the leaven-room, the temperature of which is kept at about 40° C., to bring about growth of the mold in from three to four days. They are turned once every two days. If the room temperature or the humidity is too high, the windows should be occasionally opened for ventilation. After a month, when the leaven has become covered with the mycelia of the mold, it is removed and stored in another room. The preparation of the leaven is always carried out in warm weather, the spring or summer.

Fermentation—Kao-liang (*Sorghum vulgare*) is first crushed into powder and sprinkled with water, heaped up and covered with mats for one or two days and nights, then steamed in a big wooden cooking vessel for about two hours. It is then spread on the floor in order to let it cool to about 25° C. and mixed with the powdered leaven, one part being required for three parts of *kao-liang*. Both of these, after being thoroughly mixed, are put into a large vat made of brick, capable of holding more than twenty *shih* of material. The vat is covered with a wooden cover. Some stalks of *kao-liang* are put on top, and the whole sealed with mud to the depth of more than one inch. Then the fermentation takes place gradually and by and by the surface of the covering mud collapses. This must be trampled over once or twice daily, for from eight to ten days until the fermentation is finished. The fermented mash is now ready for distillation. The distilled residue may be mixed with the new material of powdered *kao-liang* and *ch'ü* to be refermented, so that one batch of material is always employed in succession for four or five times of refermentation, until the last stage, when only the leaven is added without the addition of *kao-liang*.

Distillation—The distilling apparatus is of simple and primitive construction (Figure 83). A wooden cylinder (to hold the mash) stands in a large iron pan filled with water underneath which a fire is lit. At the top of the cylinder is fitted a tin pot containing cold water to cool the condensed spirit which is carried off by a metal pipe attached to the top part of the cylinder and is collected in a suitable vessel. In the first distillation, new *kao-liang* for the second fermentation is added to the mash and is thus steamed in such fashion that the cooking process of the *kao-liang* is carried out at the same time as the distillation. The distillate contains about 65% of pure alcohol. Nearly 35 liters of this spirit may be obtained from one *shih* of *kao-liang*.

THE ANCIENT METHOD OF PREPARING VINEGAR

Because of the readiness with which wine is converted into vinegar, it is evident that vinegar may have been produced when wine was first made.

Ch'i min yao shu 8.7a–10a describes as many as twenty methods of making vinegar. A brief survey of these is now given below.

Rice, sour wine, or damaged wine and wine-lees are all capable of being converted into vinegar. The ordinary leaven used in making wine was also used for making vinegar, because certain of the bacteria present in it can grow and reproduce to cause the acetic acid fermentation. The proper time for making vinegar was in the fifth or the seventh month of the lunar calendar. In general, one *tou* of leaven, three *tou* each of rice and water were taken as materials. According to the capacity of the fermenting jar, the amount of materials was in the same proportions in order to fill the jar. The rice was previously cooked, spread, and cooled to body temperature, then the leaven was powdered and put into the jar, followed by the water and the cooked rice. The mouth of the jar was then covered with a piece of cotton.

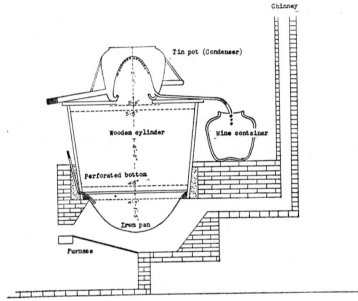

Figure 83. Still for distilling kao-liang *wine.*

One bowl of well-water was added after one week and another bowl after three weeks. The fermentation took about one month.

Either the sour wine produced from an incorrect operation or the unpressed and stored wine of damaged quality might be converted into vinegar as just stated. Generally, five *shih* of wine were diluted with one *shih* of well water and mixed with two *tou* of leaven in a jar. Two *shih* of

cooked rice were cooled to the body temperature and put in
with stirring. The mouth of the jar was sealed with cotton.
One more stirring was required after the fermentation had
begun. In the spring or summer, the fermentation was complete after one week but a longer time was required in the
autumn or winter. After settling for one month, the vinegar
was decanted and stored in other vessels.

If wine-lees were used, the fermenting process was carried out by cooking the cereal and mixing with the wine-lees.
The mixture was put into a fermenting jar to fill it, and the
jar was sealed with cotton. In summer, the outside of the
jar was sprinkled constantly with cold water in order to
lower the temperature, but in the spring or autumn it was
covered with straw or sprinkled with warm water as required.
After one week, water was added and the finished vinegar
was finally strained.

THE PRESENT METHOD OF MAKING VINEGAR IN CHINA

The process of making vinegar today resembles closely
that practiced in ancient times. *Kao-liang* and *hsiao-mi*
(小米), hulled grains of *Setaria italica*, or a mixture of both
are used as materials for making vinegar in the northern
parts of China; while *tao-mi* (稻米), unhusked rice, *no-mi*
glutinous rice, etc., are used in the southern provinces. Rice
is mixed with leaven and water to bring about an acid fermentation. Wine-lees are sometimes used. In the northern
provinces, the leaven is made in the same way as that used
for making *kao-liang* wine as previously described. The fermenting process is carried out by boiling *kao-liang* and *hsiao-
mi* with water to form a congee and putting into a jar. The
amount of the leaven required is one-fourth to that of *kao-
liang* and rice. After they have been thoroughly mixed, the
jar is covered with straw and put in a warm place. The mixture is stirred once daily. After more than one month, it is

mixed with a certain amount of rice-chaff or wheat-bran and turned over constantly by hand so as to distribute the heat uniformly. It is then stirred once or twice daily. The fermentation ceases in ten days or more. The fermented mash is later introduced into a strainer through which it is clarified with the addition of water. The strained liquid is left out-doors to freeze in the winter, throwing away the pure ice and leaving the sour liquid, or it is allowed to evaporate in the sun in the summer. As a result of either of these methods, the vinegar is concentrated and a product of excellent frag-rance is obtained.

A special method has been used in the province of Shansi for darkening the color of the vinegar. Before the process of straining, the sour mash is put into jars which are heated on stoves over mild fires placed in the middle of the fermenting room. On every stove are put two jars, which are covered with either an earthen pan or a stone slab. The mash is turned over twice in the morning and evening every day. The heating is continued until the color becomes ex-tremely dark, then it is taken out for straining.

Appendix 1—THE CHINESE DYNASTIES

The Five Rulers...............	legendary	9 rulers
Hsia.........................	legendary	17 rulers
Shang or Yin.................	before 1100 B.C.	28 rulers
Chou.........................	*ca.* 1100–255 B.C.	34 rulers
Ch'in........................	255–206 B.C.	5 rulers
Han.........................	206 B.C.–A.D. 23	14 rulers
Later Han....................	A.D. 23–220	12 rulers
The Three Kingdoms		
Minor Han................	A.D. 221	2 rulers
Wei......................	A.D. 220	5 rulers
Wu.......................	A.D. 222	4 rulers
Western Chin.................	A.D. 265–316	4 rulers
Eastern Chin.................	A.D. 317–420	11 rulers
Division between North and South	A.D. 420–589	
Liu Sung.................	A.D. 420	9 rulers
Ch'i.....................	A.D. 479	7 rulers
Liang....................	A.D. 502	6 rulers
Ch'en....................	A.D. 557	5 rulers
Northern Wei.............	A.D. 386	15 rulers
Western Wei..............	A.D. 535	3 rulers
Eastern Wei..............	A.D. 534	1 ruler
Northern Ch'i............	A.D. 550	7 rulers
Northern Chou............	A.D. 557	5 rulers
Sui.........................	A.D. 589–618	4 rulers
T'ang.......................	A.D. 618–907	22 rulers

213

The Five Dynasties..............	A.D. 907–960	
Posterior Liang................	A.D. 907	2 rulers
Posterior T'ang................	A.D. 923	4 rulers
Posterior Chin................	A.D. 936	2 rulers
Posterior Han.................	A.D. 947	2 rulers
Posterior Chou...............	A.D. 951	3 rulers
Sung.........................	A.D. 960–1126	9 rulers
Southern Sung.................	A.D. 1127–1279	9 rulers
Yüan or Mongol................	A.D. 1279–1368	9 rulers
Ming.........................	A.D. 1368–1644	17 rulers
Ch'ing or Manchu..............	A.D. 1644–1912	10 rulers
The Republic of China..........	A.D. 1912	

Appendix 2—CHINESE
WEIGHTS AND MEASURES

Measures of Weight: 1 catty (*chin* 斤) = 16 taels or Chinese ounces (*liang* 兩) = 500 grams.
1 tael = 10 mace (*ch'ien* 錢) = 31.2 grams.
1 mace = 10 candareens (*fen* 分) = 3.12 grams.
1 candareen = 0.312 gram.
100 catties = 1 picul.

Measures of Volume: 1 *shih* (石) = 10 *tou* (斗) or Chinese bushels = 100 liters.
1 *tou* = 10 *sheng* (升) or Chinese pints = 10 liters.
1 *sheng* = 1 liter.

Measures of Distance: 1 *chang* (丈) = 10 *ch'ih* (尺) or Chinese feet = 3.33 meters.
1 *ch'ih* = 10 *ts'un* (寸) or Chinese inches = 0.33 meter.
1 *ts'un* = 10 *fen* (分) = 0.033 meter.
180 *chang* = 1 *li* (里) or Chinese mile = ⅓ English mile.

Square Measure: 6 square *chang* = 1 *fen* (分).
10 *fen* (分) = 1 *mou* (畝) or Chinese acre